STECK-VAUGHN

TOP LINE *Math*

Fractions

AF732236

Harcourt Achieve
Rigby • Saxon • Steck-Vaughn

www.HarcourtAchieve.com
1.800.531.5015

Acknowledgments

Editorial Director	Ellen Northcutt
Supervising Editor	Pamela Sears
Senior Editor	Kathy Immel
Associate Design Director	Joyce Spicer
Design Team	Jim Cauthron Joan Cunningham
Photo Researcher	Stephanie Arsenault
Cover Art	©Janet Parke
Photography Credits	p. 6 Courtesy Sam Dudgeon/HRW Studio; p. 30 ©Dennis MacDonald/PhotoEdit. Additional photography by Photodisc/Getty Royalty Free.

ISBN 978-1-41-900368-4

4 5 6 7 8 9 10 1413 15 14 13 12
4500361034

Contents

To the Student

Building a solid foundation in math is your key to success in school and in the future. Working with the *Top Line Math* books will help you to develop the basic math skills that you use every day. As you build on math skills that you already know and learn new math skills, you will see how much math connects to real life.

When you read the Overview in this *Top Line Math* book, read the You Know and You Will Learn sections. As you focus on new math skills, consider how they connect to what you already know.

Pretest and Post Test

Take the Pretest at the beginning of this book. Your results on the Pretest will show you which math skills you already know and which ones you need to develop.

When you have finished working in this book, take the Post Test. Your results on the Post Test will show you how much you have learned.

Practice

Practice pages allow you to practice the skills you have learned in the lesson. You will solve both computation problems and word problems.

Unit Reviews

Unit Reviews let you see how well you have learned the skills and concepts presented in each unit.

Test–Taking Strategy

Every test-taking strategy shows you various tools you can use when taking tests.

Glossary

Each lesson has **key words** that are important to know. Turn to the glossary at the end of the book to learn the meaning of new words. Use the definitions and examples to strengthen your understanding of math terms.

Setting Goals

A goal is something you aim for, something you want to achieve. It is important to set goals throughout your life so you can plan realistic ways to get what you want.

Successful people in all fields set goals. Think about your own goals.

- Where do you see yourself after high school?
- What do you want to be doing 10 years from now?
- What steps do you need to take to get to your goals?

Goal setting is a step-by-step process. To start this process, you need to think about what you want and how you will get it. Setting a long-term goal is a way to plan for the future. A short-term goal is one of the steps you take to achieve your long-term goal.

What is your long-term goal for using this book about fractions? You may want to improve your test scores or you may want to become better at math so you can become a graphic designer.

Write your long-term goal for learning math.

____

____

Think about how you already use fractions. Then, set some short-term goals for what you would like to learn in this book. These short-term goals will help you to reach your long-term goal.

I use fractions in my everyday life to

- ☐ measure ingredients when I bake or cook.
- ☐ figure out how much pizza to order for a crowd.
- ☐ choose the right tool or make accurate measurements.
- ☐ ____________________________________

My short-term goals for using this book are

____

____

Pretest

Take this Pretest before you begin this book. Do not worry if you cannot easily answer all the questions. The Pretest will help you determine which skills you are already strong in and which skills you need to practice.

Write a fraction for each sentence.

1. Five out of 12 people in the club were absent. ____________

2. There were 24 movies playing in the multiplex theater. I saw all 24. ____________

3. Gretchen cut the pizza into 8 pieces and took 4 of them. ____________

Write each fraction in simplest form.

4. $\frac{6}{15}$ ________

5. $\frac{4}{6}$ ________

6. $\frac{6}{12}$ ________

7. $\frac{15}{18}$ ________

Find the least common denominator (LCD).

8. $\frac{1}{3}$ and $\frac{1}{6}$

9. $\frac{1}{2}$ and $\frac{5}{6}$

10. $\frac{1}{4}$ and $\frac{3}{7}$

11. $\frac{4}{5}$ and $\frac{1}{2}$

Add. Simplify if necessary.

12. Darren ate $\frac{1}{8}$ of a gallon of ice cream. His brother Darrell ate $\frac{3}{8}$ of the gallon. How much ice cream did they eat all together?

13. $\frac{2}{5} + \frac{3}{10} =$

14. $3\frac{5}{8} + 2\frac{1}{2} =$

Subtract. Simplify if necessary.

15. $\frac{5}{8} - \frac{3}{8} =$

16. Aria had $\frac{1}{2}$ of a bag of apples. She gave $\frac{1}{6}$ of her apples away. What fraction of the bag of apples was left?

17. $6\frac{1}{3} - 2\frac{5}{6} =$

Multiply. Simplify if necessary.

18. How much is $\frac{3}{4}$ of $\frac{7}{8}$?

19. $\frac{9}{10} \times \frac{5}{6} =$

20. $1\frac{1}{3} \times 1\frac{2}{3} =$

21. $3\frac{1}{8} \times 3\frac{1}{5} =$

Divide. Simplify if necessary.

22. $\frac{2}{3} \div \frac{1}{3} =$

23. How many times does $\frac{1}{4}$ go into $\frac{5}{8}$?

24. $2\frac{1}{2} \div 1\frac{1}{2} =$

25. $2\frac{4}{5} \div 1\frac{1}{2} =$

UNIT 1 Understanding Fractions

Real-Life Matters

You use fractions every day. When you tell a friend that you want only $\frac{1}{2}$ a glass of milk, or that you will be $\frac{3}{4}$ of an hour late for the concert, or that it is a $2\frac{1}{3}$-mile drive to the meeting on Friday night, you are using fractions. Whenever you use a ruler or a measuring cup, you are probably using fractions to measure.

Real-Life Application

Your friends are coming over Friday night to watch a movie. You want to make some tacos for the party. Your recipe makes 12 tacos but you want to double the recipe. How would you double the ingredients?

____

____

The tacos should be baked in a $9\frac{1}{2}$-inch $\times$ $13\frac{1}{2}$-inch pan. You look at your pan and wonder if it is the correct size. How would you make sure?

____

____

Your recipe says to bake one batch of tacos for $\frac{3}{4}$ of an hour. Because you are going to make 2 batches, you will need to add another $\frac{3}{4}$ of an hour to your schedule. How much time will you need to bake the 2 batches of tacos?

____

____

The recipe calls for 0.5 teaspoon of salt. Your friend tells you to use the $\frac{1}{2}$-teaspoon measuring spoon. Explain why your friend is correct.

____

____

Overview • Lessons 1–4

Fractions

You already know how to add, subtract, multiply and divide whole numbers. You can learn to do the same operations with fractions. Knowing how to work with fractions is a useful everyday skill. For example, you may need $\frac{3}{4}$ cup of milk for a recipe. You may need $\frac{1}{2}$ of a yard of ribbon to make a costume. You may need to use a $\frac{3}{16}$-inch wrench for a shop project.

A **fraction** is a number that names part of a whole or part of a group. Every fraction shows 2 numbers. One number describes the part and the other number describes the whole. For example:

$$\frac{\text{part}}{\text{whole}} = \frac{3}{16}$$

The top number of a fraction is called a **numerator.**
The bottom number of a fraction is called a **denominator.**

$$\frac{3}{16} \begin{array}{l} \leftarrow \text{numerator} \\ \leftarrow \text{denominator} \end{array}$$

YOU KNOW

- That each product in a multiplication table is a multiple
- That a number multiplied or divided by 1 remains the same number
- How to find the greatest common factor (GCF) of 2 numbers

YOU WILL LEARN

- How to write fractions to represent part of a whole or a group
- How to find the least common multiple
- How to find equivalent fractions
- How to compare and order fractions.

Remember the BASICS

Multiply.

1. 12 × 3 = 36 **2.** 24 × 6 = **3.** 19 × 4 =

4. 16 × 11 = **5.** 32 × 13 = **6.** 63 × 2 =

Divide.

7. 15 ÷ 3 = 5 **8.** 22 ÷ 11 = **9.** 20 ÷ 4 =

10. 63 ÷ 7 = **11.** 121 ÷ 11 = **12.** 483 ÷ 21 =

LESSON 1 Understanding Fractions

A fraction is a way of comparing part of a group to the whole group.

Three of the 7 number cards show the number 1. You can also say that $\frac{3}{7}$ of the cards in the group of cards show the number 1.

In the fraction $\frac{3}{7}$, the number 3 shows part of the group. This number is called the **numerator.**

The total number of cards is called the **denominator.**

$$\frac{\text{part}}{\text{whole}} = \frac{\text{numerator}}{\text{denominator}} = \frac{3}{7}$$

Example

A pizza is cut into 8 equal slices. You and your friends eat 5 slices. Write a fraction to show the part of the pizza that is left.

STEP 1 Identify the denominator.

The total number of slices is the whole. The pizza was cut into a total of 8 slices, so the denominator is 8.

$\frac{\ }{8}$

STEP 2 Identify the numerator.

The part of the whole is the numerator. There are 3 pieces of pizza left, so the numerator is 3.

$\frac{3}{8}$

STEP 3 Write the fraction.

$$\frac{\text{part}}{\text{whole}} = \frac{\text{numerator}}{\text{denominator}} = \frac{3}{8}$$

$\frac{3}{8}$ of the pizza is left.

ON YOUR OWN

Three of the last 5 songs on the radio were hits from last year. Write a fraction to show how many of the songs were hits from last year.

Practice

Part is the top number. The whole is the bottom number.

Building Skills

Write a fraction.

1. What part of a dollar is shown? $\frac{3}{4}$

2. Of all the fruit shown, what fraction is apples?

3. What fraction of a gallon is shown? (4 quarts = 1 gallon)

4. This cake was cut into 12 pieces. What fraction of the cake is left?

Write a fraction.

5. Out of 18 friends at the picnic, 11 live on the same street.

6. A dozen is equal to 12. What part of a dozen is 11?

7. There are 12 cats living at the farm. Of these, 7 are female.

8. If a day is equal to 24 hours, what part of a day is 8 hours?

9. If a foot is equal to 12 inches, what part of a foot is 7 inches?

10. There are 24 students in the class. Nineteen of the 24 students are right-handed.

Problem Solving

Solve.

11. Jessica works 40 hours per week. So far this week, she has worked 9 hours. What part of her workweek has she completed?

$\frac{9}{40}$

12. One hour is equal to 60 minutes. What part of an hour is 40 minutes?

13. Tanya can fit 16 pictures on each page of her photo album. If she has 12 pictures, what fraction of a page will she need to use?

14. Devon hit 57 free throws in 60 tries. What fraction of free throws did he complete?

LESSON 2 Equivalent Fractions

Sometimes 2 fractions can have the same value even when they do not look the same. Look at the 2 pizzas. They are the same size. One pizza has 8 slices. The other has 4 slices. The pizzas have different numbers of slices but the amount of the whole pizza is the same. The 2 pizzas are equal or **equivalent.** Now look at the part of each pizza covered with onions.

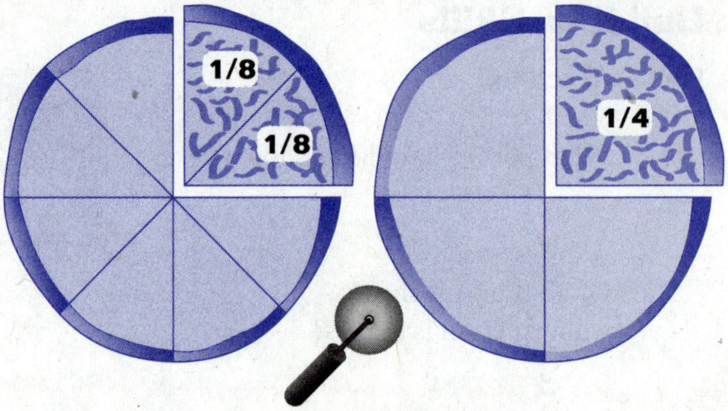

We can use an equivalent fraction to describe the pizza slices with onions.

$\frac{\text{2 slices}}{\text{8 slices}} = \frac{\text{1 slice}}{\text{4 slices}}$ or

$\frac{2}{8} = \frac{1}{4}$

Equivalent fractions name the same amount. You make fractions equivalent by multiplying or dividing the numerator and denominator by the same number.

Example

Find an equivalent fraction for $\frac{6}{16}$.

STEP 1 **Choose a number that you can multiply or divide into both the numerator and denominator.**
You can multiply both 6 and 16 by 2.

STEP 2 **Multiply or divide the numerator and denominator.**
Multiply the numerator and denominator by the same number, 2.

$$\frac{6}{16} \times \frac{2}{2} = \frac{12}{32}$$

STEP 3 **Write the equivalent fractions.**
$\frac{12}{32}$ **is equivalent to** $\frac{6}{16}$

$$\frac{6}{16} = \frac{12}{32}$$

ON YOUR OWN

Find an equivalent fraction for $\frac{10}{12}$.

Practice

Building Skills

Find an equivalent fraction.

1. $\frac{4}{8}$ $\div \frac{4}{4} = \frac{1}{2}$ **2.** $\frac{10}{15}$ **3.** $\frac{6}{12}$ **4.** $\frac{18}{24}$

Circle the equivalent fraction.

5. $\frac{1}{2} = \frac{3}{10}$ $\frac{6}{12}$ $\frac{4}{7}$ $\frac{3}{9}$ $\frac{2}{8}$

6. $\frac{3}{5} = \frac{3}{10}$ $\frac{7}{12}$ $\frac{6}{10}$ $\frac{6}{20}$ $\frac{10}{15}$

7. $\frac{2}{3} = \frac{8}{10}$ $\frac{6}{9}$ $\frac{4}{12}$ $\frac{3}{9}$ $\frac{2}{24}$

8. $\frac{9}{10} = \frac{3}{4}$ $\frac{18}{21}$ $\frac{4}{5}$ $\frac{3}{9}$ $\frac{27}{30}$

Problem Solving

Find the equivalent fraction.

9. Manny has read 6 of the 10 books in a popular mystery series. How many fifths is this?

$\frac{6}{10} = \frac{3}{5}$

10. Anna has converted $\frac{5}{8}$ of her old videocassettes to DVDs. How many sixteenths is this?

11. Vinny shelved 30 of the 40 books that were returned to the library today. How many fourths is this?

12. Raquel invited 20 people to her party and 16 of them showed up. Write an equivalent fraction to describe how many of the invited people came to the party.

13. You have collected 25 of the 50 state quarters. Write an equivalent fraction to show this number.

14. You did 25 of the 30 push-ups required in gym class. Find an equivalent fraction when 5 is the numerator.

LESSON 3 Least Common Multiple

Suppose you do volunteer work at a local food pantry every 5 days. Your friend volunteers there every 4 days. How often will the two of you work together in the first month? First compare the multiples of 5 and 4. (The multiples they have in common are in blue.) Then find the lowest multiple that 4 and 5 have in common.

5: 5, 10, 15, 20, 25, 30, 35, 40, 45, 50
4: 4, 8, 12, 16, 20, 24, 28, 32, 36, 40

The **least common multiple** (LCM) of 4 and 5 is 20.

If you get to work together every 20 days, then in 1 month you will work together on 1 day.

Example

Matt plays the piano every 3 days. Lola plays the piano every 4 days. If they both played today, on what day will they both play again?

STEP 1 List several multiples of the larger number.

4: 4, 8, 12, 16, 20, 24, 28, 32

STEP 2 List several multiples of the smaller number.

3: 3, 6, 9, 12, 15, 18, 21, 24

STEP 3 Find the multiple or multiples that are common to both numbers.

4: 4, 8, 12, 16, 20, 24, 28, 32
3: 3, 6, 9, 12, 15, 18, 21, 24

The multiples common to both 3 and 4 are 12 and 24.

STEP 4 Compare the multiples. The multiple that is lower in value is the least common multiple.

$12 < 24$

Twelve is the least multiple they have in common. So the LCM of 3 and 4 is 12. Matt and Lola will both play the piano on the twelfth day.

ON YOUR OWN

Rachel swims 10 laps every fourth day and uses free weights every fifth day. If she did both today, in how many days will she once again swim 10 laps and use free weights on the same day?

Practice

Building Skills

Find the least common multiple (LCM) for each pair of numbers.

1. 9 and 12

12: 12, 24, 36, 48
9: 9, 18, 27, 36, 45

The LCM of 9 and 12 is 36.

2. 4 and 8

3. 6 and 9

4. 8 and 9

5. 6 and 8

6. 10 and 15

7. 6 and 7

8. 5 and 8

9. 4 and 10

Problem Solving

Use the LCM to solve these problems.

10. Jared finishes a book in 6 days. Marta finishes a book in 4 days. If they both start reading on the same day, how many days will it take before they both finish a book on the same day?

The LCM of 4 and 6 is 12.
They will finish a book on the 12th day.

11. Juan receives a news e-mail every 7 days and a music e-mail every 5 days. He received both of them today. In how many more days will he again receive both e-mails on the same day?

12. During rush hour, the express bus arrives every 8 minutes, while the regular bus comes every 10 minutes. If both buses just went by, how many more minutes will it take for both of them to again show up at the same time?

13. Nakita goes to swim practice every second day. Emily goes to swim practice every seventh day. If they both went to practice today, in how many days will they both go to practice again?

14. Your training program requires you to run every second day and to weight train every third day. What is the next day on which you will have to run and weight train?

15. Damon does dark laundry every 3 days and light laundry every 5 days. How often does he have to do both loads on the same day?

LESSON 4 Comparing and Ordering Fractions

At lunch you decide to share 2 granola bars with your friends. One friend gets $\frac{2}{3}$ of 1 bar. The other friend gets $\frac{3}{4}$ of the other bar. Look at the granola bars. You can see that $\frac{3}{4} > \frac{2}{3}$

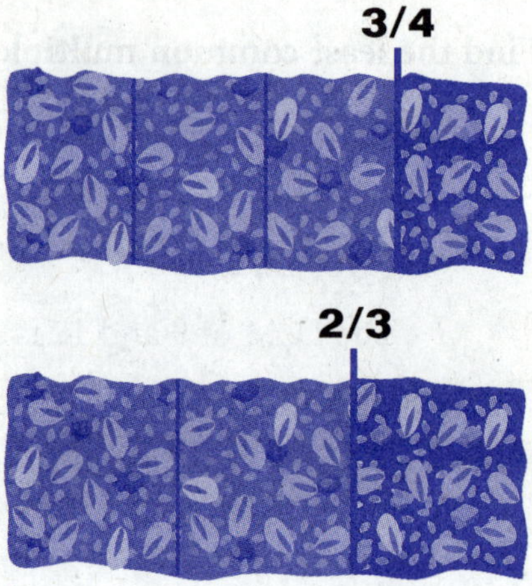

To compare fractions, the fractions must have the same denominator. You can use your knowledge of equivalent fractions to rewrite each fraction, so that it has same denominator. To find the common denominator, use the least common multiple (LCM) of the denominators. This is also called the **least common denominator** (LCD). When the denominators are the same, compare the numerators to see which fraction is greater.

$$\frac{\text{numerator}}{\text{denominator}} = \frac{3}{4}$$

Example

Compare. Use <, >, or = signs.

$\frac{3}{7}\ \frac{2}{5}$

STEP 1 **Find the least common denominator (LCD).**

List the multiples of 5 and 7.

5: 5, 10, 15, 20, 25, 30, 35, 40. . .

7: 7, 14, 21, 28, 35, 42, 49, 56. . .

The least common multiple (LCM) of the denominators is 35. So the LCD is 35.

STEP 2 **Write equivalent fractions using the LCD as the new denominator.**

$\frac{3}{7} = \frac{\quad}{35}$ $\frac{2}{5} = \frac{\quad}{35}$

STEP 3 **Divide the LCD by the denominators.**

$35 \div 7 = 5$ $35 \div 5 = 7$

STEP 4 **Multiply the numerator and denominator of each fraction by the answers in Step 3.**

$\frac{3}{7} \times \frac{5}{5} = \frac{15}{35}$ $\frac{2}{5} \times \frac{7}{7} = \frac{14}{35}$

STEP 5 **Compare the numerators.**

$\frac{3}{7} > \frac{2}{5}$

$15 > 14$, so $\frac{15}{35} > \frac{14}{35}$

ON YOUR OWN

Kirsten has completed $\frac{1}{3}$ of her homework. Brendan has completed $\frac{2}{5}$ of his homework. Use <, >, or = to show who has completed more homework.

Practice

Find the LCD and then compare the numerators.

Building Skills

Compare. Use >, <, or = signs.

1. $\frac{5}{6}$ [>] $\frac{1}{4}$

$\frac{10}{12} > \frac{3}{12}; \frac{5}{6} > \frac{1}{4}$

2. $\frac{1}{5}$ [ ] $\frac{2}{10}$

3. $\frac{3}{4}$ [ ] $\frac{7}{8}$

4. $\frac{4}{5}$ [ ] $\frac{2}{3}$

5. $\frac{2}{5}$ [ ] $\frac{1}{2}$

6. $\frac{3}{8}$ [ ] $\frac{1}{4}$

7. $\frac{9}{10}$ [ ] $\frac{3}{4}$

8. $\frac{3}{6}$ [ ] $\frac{4}{12}$

9. $\frac{5}{8}$ [ ] $\frac{3}{7}$

Write these fractions in order from least to greatest.

10. $\frac{2}{5}, \frac{7}{10}, \frac{1}{2}$

$\frac{2}{5} = \frac{4}{10}$ $\frac{7}{10} = \frac{7}{10}$ $\frac{1}{2} = \frac{5}{10}$

$\frac{4}{10} < \frac{5}{10} < \frac{7}{10}$ so $\frac{2}{5} < \frac{1}{2} < \frac{7}{10}$

11. $\frac{2}{3}, \frac{5}{6}, \frac{1}{2}$

Problem Solving

Solve each problem.

12. Lamont stayed at the game for $\frac{1}{2}$ hour. Jerry was there for $\frac{3}{4}$ hour. Who stayed at the game longer?

$\frac{1}{2} = \frac{2}{4}; \frac{2}{4} < \frac{3}{4}$

Jerry stayed at the game longer.

13. Christine rode her bike $\frac{4}{5}$ of a mile. Barbara ran $\frac{9}{10}$ of a mile. Gary jogged $\frac{1}{2}$ mile. Who traveled the farthest?

14. One type of juice provides $\frac{2}{3}$ of a person's daily requirement of vitamin C. Another provides $\frac{3}{4}$ of the daily requirement. Which juice is less nutritious?

15. Suppose you have to organize wrenches by size. Place these three wrenches in order from smallest to largest: $\frac{1}{4}$ inch, $\frac{3}{16}$ inch, $\frac{1}{8}$ inch.

TEST–TAKING STRATEGY

Make a Table

You can make a table to answer test questions about equivalent fractions.

Example

Sarah walked $\frac{3}{8}$ mile from the airport parking lot to the baggage check-in. Then she walked $\frac{15}{40}$ mile to the waiting area. Is the distance Sarah walked to the waiting area equivalent to the distance she walked to the baggage check-in?

You can create a table that shows all the fractions equivalent to $\frac{3}{8}$.

STEP 1 List multiples of 3 and 8 in the table to show fractions equivalent to $\frac{3}{8}$.

	×2	×3	×4	×5	×6
3	6	9	12	15	18
8	16	24	32	40	48

Multiples in the same column form fractions equivalent to $\frac{3}{8}$.

Based on the table, you see that $\frac{3}{8}$, $\frac{6}{16}$, $\frac{9}{24}$, $\frac{12}{32}$, $\frac{15}{40}$, and $\frac{18}{48}$ are all equivalent fractions.

STEP 2 Look for $\frac{15}{40}$ in the table.

$\frac{15}{40}$ is in the table, so $\frac{15}{40}$ is equivalent to $\frac{3}{8}$.

The distance Sarah walked to the waiting area is equivalent to the distance she walked to the baggage check-in.

TRY IT OUT

A pattern for making a backpack calls for $\frac{2}{3}$ yard of denim. If Trevor bought an equivalent amount of denim, how much did he buy?

Circle the correct answer.

A. $\frac{3}{6}$ B. $\frac{12}{18}$ C. $\frac{15}{24}$ D. $\frac{36}{45}$

Option B is correct.

	× 3	× 4	× 5	× 6
2	6	8	10	12
3	9	12	15	18

Overview • Lessons 5–7

Mixed Numbers

You are going down the highway. A sign says that the next 2 exits are $\frac{1}{2}$ mile and $2\frac{1}{2}$ miles away.

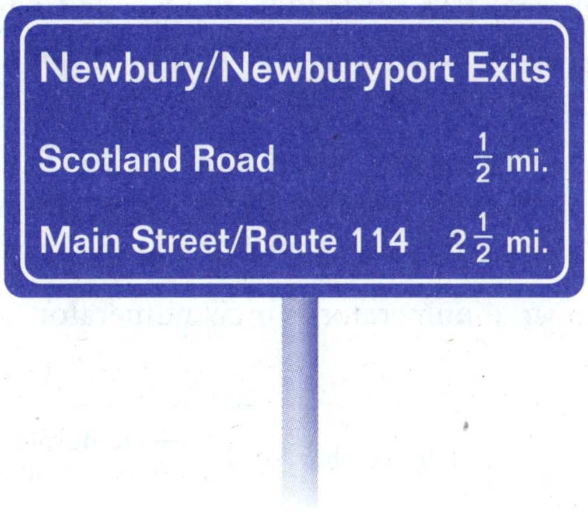

You learned that $\frac{1}{2}$ is a fraction. It is a **proper fraction** because the numerator is smaller than the denominator. $2\frac{1}{2}$ is a mixed number. A **mixed number** is a whole number and a proper fraction.

whole number → $2\frac{1}{2}$ ← numerator / ← denominator

YOU KNOW

- How to simplify fractions
- That when the numerator is the same as the denominator, the fraction equals 1

YOU WILL LEARN

- How to rename an improper fraction
- How to change mixed numbers into improper fractions
- How to simplify mixed numbers

Remember the BASICS

Simplify each fraction.

1. $\frac{4}{10} =$

   $\frac{4}{10} \div \frac{2}{2} = \frac{2}{5}$

2. $\frac{3}{6} =$

3. $\frac{16}{18} =$

4. $\frac{9}{9} =$

5. $\frac{8}{16} =$

6. $\frac{12}{15} =$

7. $\frac{10}{10} =$

8. $\frac{15}{20} =$

9. $\frac{21}{24} =$

10. $\frac{16}{16} =$

11. $\frac{14}{21} =$

12. $\frac{20}{25} =$

13. $\frac{24}{30} =$

14. $\frac{20}{20} =$

15. $\frac{15}{24} =$

16. $\frac{30}{40} =$

LESSON 5 Mixed Numbers as Improper Fractions

A mixed number is a number written as a whole number and a fraction. An **improper fraction** is a fraction whose numerator is *equal to or greater than* its denominator. For example, $\frac{11}{10}$, $\frac{3}{2}$, $\frac{7}{4}$, and $\frac{20}{20}$ are improper fractions.

An improper fraction can be written as a mixed number. To change a mixed number into an improper fraction, multiply the whole number by the denominator and then add the numerator. The answer is your new numerator. You keep the original denominator.

denominator × whole number + numerator = new numerator

or

$$3\frac{1}{2} \rightarrow \frac{(2 \times 3) + 1}{2} = \frac{7}{2}$$

whole number $\rightarrow 2\frac{1}{2}$ $\leftarrow$ numerator / $\leftarrow$ denominator

Example

Write $4\frac{1}{3}$ as an improper fraction.

STEP 1 Multiply the denominator by the whole number.

$3 \times 4 = 12$

STEP 2 Add the numerator.

$12 + 1 = 13$

STEP 3 Write that total as the numerator, keeping the denominator the same.

$4\frac{1}{3}$ written on an improper fraction is $\frac{13}{3}$.

$\frac{13}{3}$

ON YOUR OWN

Write $3\frac{5}{8}$ as an improper fraction.

Practice

The denominator of the mixed number is the denominator of the improper fraction.

Building Skills

Write each mixed number as an improper fraction.

1. $2\frac{5}{8} =$ $2 \times 8 = 16$; $16 + 5 = 21$; $2\frac{5}{8} = \frac{21}{8}$

2. $3\frac{4}{5} =$

3. $4\frac{5}{6} =$

4. $2\frac{9}{10} =$

5. $6\frac{2}{3} =$

6. $4\frac{1}{2} =$

7. $3\frac{2}{5} =$

8. $4\frac{1}{8} =$

9. $1\frac{7}{8} =$

Problem Solving

Write each mixed number as an improper fraction.

10. Milagro needs to add $2\frac{1}{4}$ quarts of oil to her car's engine. Change $2\frac{1}{4}$ to an improper fraction.

$(2 \times 4) + 1 = 9$; $2\frac{1}{4} = \frac{9}{4}$

11. The baseball game was rained out after $4\frac{2}{3}$ innings. Change $4\frac{2}{3}$ to an improper fraction.

12. Lily bought $1\frac{5}{8}$ pounds of egg salad. How many eighths of egg salad did she buy?

13. Emile's band rehearsed for $1\frac{1}{2}$ hours. How many half-hours was that?

14. Julia ran $2\frac{1}{4}$ miles around the track. How many $\frac{1}{4}$-mile laps did she run?

15. George has $2\frac{3}{4}$ yards of electrical wire. He wants to cut the wire into $\frac{1}{4}$-yard lengths. How many pieces of wire will he get?

LESSON 6 Renaming Improper Fractions

Just as you can **rename**, or change, a mixed number to an improper fraction, you can change an improper fraction to a mixed number. When you see an improper fraction, divide the numerator by the denominator. The result is the whole number part of your mixed number. Any remainder is the numerator of the proper fraction.

You can think of the fraction bar as a division sign.

$\frac{19}{4}$ means *nineteen divided by four.*

All fractions should be reduced to **simplest form**, or when both the numerator and denominator cannot be divided evenly any further.

Example

Change $\frac{19}{4}$ to a mixed number.

$\frac{19}{4} \rightarrow \frac{\text{numerator}}{\text{denominator}}$

STEP 1 **Divide the numerator by the denominator.**
The first step of dividing gives you the whole number part of the mixed number.

$$\begin{array}{r} 4 \\ 4\overline{)19} \\ -\underline{16} \\ 3R \end{array}$$

STEP 2 **The remainder then becomes the numerator of the fraction.**
The remainder of 3 is the numerator in $4\frac{3}{4}$.

STEP 3 **Simplify the fraction if necessary.**
The fraction $\frac{3}{4}$ is in simplest form.

Therefore $\frac{19}{4} = 4\frac{3}{4}$.

ON YOUR OWN

Change $\frac{16}{10}$ to a mixed number.

Practice

Building Skills

Rename each improper fraction.

1. $\frac{17}{10}$

$10\overline{)17} = 1R7; \frac{17}{10} = 1\frac{7}{10}$

2. $\frac{23}{5}$

3. $\frac{18}{6}$

4. $\frac{21}{4}$

5. $\frac{45}{8}$

6. $\frac{37}{7}$

7. $\frac{29}{6}$

8. $\frac{61}{8}$

9. $\frac{47}{5}$

Problem Solving

Solve.

10. Linda said she could put a toy together in 90 seconds. What part of a minute is this? (1 minute = 60 seconds)

$\frac{90}{60} = 60\overline{)90} = 1R30$

$1\frac{30}{60} = 1\frac{1}{2}$ minutes

11. Jake walked for $\frac{7}{4}$ of an hour for exercise. Rewrite this improper fraction.

12. Vilma made 5 quarts of chili for the family reunion. How many gallons is this? (4 quarts = 1 gallon)

13. How many pairs of socks can be made from a laundry pile of 27 socks?

14. The student council is selling note cards in sets of 9. How would 64 cards be packaged? Write the answer as a mixed number.

15. Zach has to cut wooden molding into 9 pieces that are each half a yard long. What is the total length of the molding written as a mixed number?

LESSON 7 Writing Mixed Numbers in Simplest Form

When you look at a mixed number, pay special attention to the fraction. Look for 2 things:

- Is the fraction proper or improper?
- Is the fraction in simplest form?

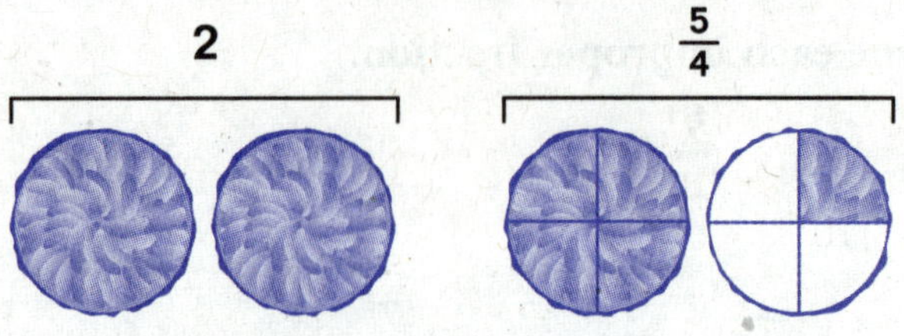

If the fraction is improper:

- Divide the numerator by the denominator.
- Add the whole number part of the answer to the existing whole number.
- Use the remainder as the numerator of the fraction.
- Keep the denominator the same as when you started.

If the fraction is a proper fraction:

- Find a number that divides evenly into the numerator and denominator.
- Divide the numerator and denominator by this number.
- Rewrite the mixed number including the simplified fraction.

Example

Simplify $5\frac{10}{8}$.

STEP 1 Is the fraction proper or improper?
The fraction is improper because the numerator is larger than the denominator.

STEP 2 Write the improper fraction as a mixed number.
$10 \div 8 = 1R2 \rightarrow 1\frac{2}{8}$

STEP 3 Add the renamed improper fraction to the whole number you started with.

$5 + 1\frac{2}{8} = 6\frac{2}{8}$

STEP 4 Simplify the fraction if necessary.
The fraction $\frac{2}{8}$ is not in simplest terms. To simplify, divide both the numerator and denominator by a number that divides evenly into both, 2.

$\frac{2}{8} \div \frac{2}{2} = \frac{1}{4}$ So $5\frac{10}{8} = 6\frac{1}{4}$.

$5\frac{10}{3}$ is equivalent to $6\frac{1}{4}$.

ON YOUR OWN

Neil has two pieces of speaker cable with a combined length of $2\frac{15}{12}$ inches. Simplify the mixed number.

Practice

Building Skills

Rename each mixed number in simplest form.

1. $3\frac{12}{10}$

$\frac{12}{10} = 12 \div 10 = 1R2$

$\frac{12}{10} = 1\frac{2}{10}$

$3 + 1\frac{2}{10} = 4\frac{2}{10} = 4\frac{1}{5}$

2. $2\frac{6}{8}$

3. $6\frac{4}{6}$

4. $5\frac{9}{6}$

5. $2\frac{5}{10}$

6. $4\frac{12}{16}$

7. $7\frac{9}{12}$

8. $3\frac{10}{8}$

9. $5\frac{8}{12}$

Problem Solving

Write each mixed number in simplest form.

10. After a week of pet sitting, Bik has $2\frac{4}{8}$ cans of dog food left. Write this mixed number in simplest form.

$\frac{4}{8} \div \frac{4}{4} = \frac{1}{2}$

Bik has $2\frac{1}{2}$ cans of dog food left.

11. The cafeteria used $8\frac{12}{10}$ gallons of pancake batter for the charity breakfast. What is this number in simplest form?

12. Amanda ran the race in $30\frac{6}{10}$ seconds. Write this number in simplest form.

13. The users of the computer room went through $7\frac{20}{25}$ packages of printer paper last week. What is this number in simplest form?

14. Wen-wa has $5\frac{12}{16}$ yards of material. Write this number in simplest form.

15. Amy says she has $7\frac{12}{10}$ boxes of comic books. How many boxes does she really have?

TEST-TAKING STRATEGY

Draw a Diagram

Drawing a diagram will help you answer test questions about mixed numbers.

Example

Frank is driving his friends to a football game. He leaves his house and drives $1\frac{1}{4}$ miles east to pick up Pedro. They drive $2\frac{3}{4}$ miles north and $1\frac{3}{4}$ miles west to pick up Ling. They all drive $1\frac{1}{2}$ miles south and $\frac{1}{2}$ mile east to the football stadium. After the game, Frank drives everyone to his house. How many miles do they drive to Frank's house?

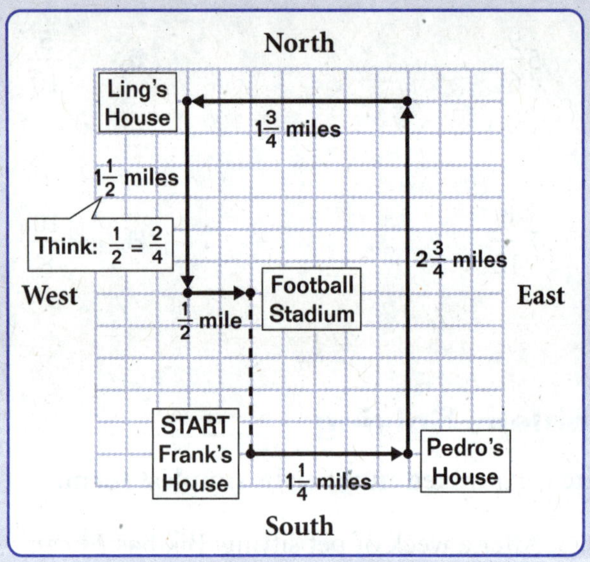

STEP 1 **Draw a diagram of the route Frank followed when he drove his friends to the football stadium. Let each square on the grid stand for $\frac{1}{4}$ mile. Hint: 4 squares = 1 mile.** On the grid, east is to the right and west is to the left; north is to the top and south is to the bottom.

STEP 2 **Use your diagram to find the distance from the football stadium to Frank's house.** You know that 1 square = $\frac{1}{4}$ mile. Using the grid you see it is 5 squares to Frank's house. Therefore, it is $\frac{5}{4}$ or $1\frac{1}{4}$ miles.

They drive $1\frac{1}{4}$ miles to Frank's house.

TRY IT OUT

Lenore is running errands around town. She rides her bike $2\frac{1}{4}$ miles south from her house to the post office. Then she rides $1\frac{1}{4}$ miles east and $2\frac{3}{4}$ miles north to the library. If she leaves the library and rides $\frac{1}{4}$ mile south, how many miles will she be from her house?

Circle the correct answer.

A. $\frac{1}{4}$ mile **B.** $1\frac{1}{4}$ miles **C.** $1\frac{1}{2}$ miles **D.** $2\frac{1}{4}$ miles

Option B is correct. When Lenore rides $\frac{1}{4}$ mile south from the library, she is $\frac{5}{4}$, or $1\frac{1}{4}$, miles from her house.

Overview • Lesson 8

Fractions and Decimals

Fractions

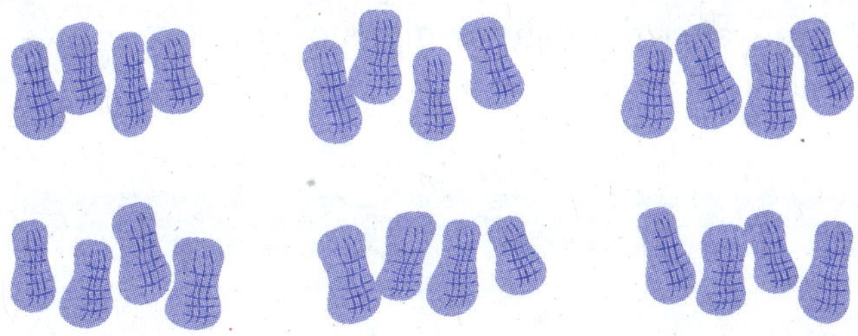

You have already learned about operations with whole numbers including division. Fractions are another way of showing division. To share 24 peanuts among 6 friends you would divide.

$24 \div 6 \qquad 6\overline{)24} \qquad \frac{24}{6}$

As you can see, there are three different ways of writing the same operation. The last is written as a fraction. In each case the value is 4.

You can use division to change fractions to decimals and decimals to fractions.

Fractions show parts of a whole. Decimals also show part of a whole. Later on you will learn more about operations with decimals.

YOU KNOW

- How to divide whole numbers
- How to simplify fractions

YOU WILL LEARN

- How to change a fraction to a decimal

Remember the BASICS

Simplify each fraction.

1. $\frac{12}{100}$

   $\frac{12}{100} \div \frac{4}{4} = \frac{3}{25}$

2. $\frac{35}{100}$

3. $\frac{125}{1000}$

4. $\frac{92}{100}$

Divide and show any remainder.

5. $5\overline{)62}$ 12R2

6. $3\overline{)45}$

7. $6\overline{)93}$

8. $3\overline{)29}$

LESSON 8 Fractions and Decimals

A fraction is a way to show division. To change a fraction to a decimal, divide the numerator by the denominator until the answer ends evenly or the final digit(s) repeat. Remember to put a decimal point followed by at least 2 zeros after the digit or digits of the numerator to set up the division.

$\frac{3}{4} = 3 \div 4;\ 4\overline{)3.00}$ with quotient 0.75

denominator $\overline{)\text{numerator}}$

Example 1

Change $\frac{7}{8}$ to a decimal.

STEP 1 Divide the numerator by the denominator.
Write a decimal point after the amount being divided, and add zeros.

STEP 2 Write a decimal point in the quotient (the answer).
Write the decimal point directly above the decimal point in the amount being divided.

$$\frac{7}{8} = 0.875$$

$8\overline{)7.000}$ with quotient $.875$
−64
60
−56
40
−40

To write a decimal as a fraction, write the decimal number as the numerator but do not include the decimal point. In the denominator, write a 1 followed by as many zeros as the number of digits behind the decimal point. Simplify the fraction if necessary.

Example 2

Change 0.225 to a fraction.

STEP 1 Write the decimal number without the decimal point as the numerator.
$\frac{225}{\ }$

STEP 2 Write a 1 and add zeros.
Count the number of places after the decimal point in the original number. In this problem, there are 3 places. You would add 3 zeros after the 1.

$\frac{225}{1000}$

STEP 3 Simplify the fraction as necessary.

$$0.225 = \frac{9}{40}$$

$$\frac{225}{1000} \div \frac{25}{25} = \frac{9}{40}$$

ON YOUR OWN

Change $\frac{5}{8}$ to a decimal.

Practice

Building Skills

Write each decimal as a fraction and each fraction as a decimal.

1. $\frac{1}{3} =$

> $3\overline{)1.00}$ with quotient .333 $= 0.\overline{3}$
> The line above the digit means it repeats.

2. $\frac{3}{8} =$

3. $\frac{4}{5} =$

4. $0.95 =$

5. $0.125 =$

6. $0.72 =$

7. $\frac{2}{3} =$

8. $\frac{7}{25} =$

9. $0.625 =$

Problem Solving

Solve each problem by changing the fraction to a decimal or the decimal to a fraction.

10. Maria has 3 quarters. What part of a dollar is 3 quarters? Write this as a decimal.

> There are 4 quarters in a dollar so 4 is the denominator. She has $\frac{3}{4}$ of a dollar, or 0.75.

11. Bret only had to time to complete $\frac{7}{8}$ of his run today. Write this as a decimal.

12. The students bought the books for $\frac{25}{70}$ of the original cost. Show the discount as a decimal.

13. Elian ate $\frac{5}{6}$ of his pizza. How do you write that as a decimal?

14. Jennie spent $0.85 on a juice drink. Write this as a fraction.

15. Phil finished 0.65 of his homework. Write the decimal as a fraction.

TEST–TAKING STRATEGY

Estimate with Fractions

Using estimation with fractions can often help you to solve a problem.

Example

Carpenters were moving some boards in a truck. The truck that carried the boards can hold no more than $52\frac{3}{4}$ pounds. Each board weighs $3\frac{1}{2}$ pounds. What is the maximum number of boards that the carpenters can move at one time?

STEP 1 Round all fractions.

- If the fraction is greater than or equal to $\frac{1}{2}$, drop the fraction and add 1. (round up)
- If the fraction is less than $\frac{1}{2}$, drop it. (round down)

$52\frac{3}{4} \rightarrow 53$

$3\frac{1}{2} \rightarrow 4$

STEP 2 Solve using the estimated numbers.

$53 \div 4 = 13$

STEP 3 Solve the problem using the mixed fractions.

Since you cannot have part of a board, you round down. You can load 15 boards onto the truck. Looking back at your estimate you see that 15 is close to your estimate, 13.

$$52\frac{3}{4} \div 3\frac{1}{2} = \frac{211}{4} \div \frac{7}{2}$$

$$\frac{211}{4} \times \frac{2}{7} = \frac{422}{28} = 15\frac{2}{28}$$

TRY IT OUT

Carla used a new plant food on the tomato plants in her garden. Each week she uses $2\frac{1}{4}$ cup of plant food. The growing season for her tomatoes is 20 weeks. How many cups of plant food will she need?

Circle the correct answer.

A. 10 cups **B.** 50 cups **C.** 45 cups **D.** 30 cups

Option C is correct. Use estimation to multiply.

Write the proper or improper fraction that names the shaded part.

1. 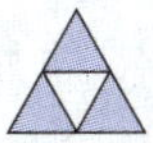 ______

2.  ______

3. 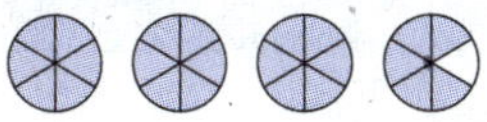 ______

4.  ______

Write the mixed number that names the shaded part.

5.  ______

6.  ______

Change each fraction to a whole number or mixed number.

7. $\frac{9}{4} =$ **8.** $\frac{15}{12} =$ **9.** $\frac{22}{5} =$ **10.** $\frac{33}{6} =$

Change each mixed number to an improper fraction.

11. $3\frac{1}{4} =$ **12.** $2\frac{5}{8} =$ **13.** $7\frac{1}{2} =$ **14.** $10\frac{3}{4} =$

Simplify each fraction.

15. $\frac{10}{12} =$ **16.** $\frac{9}{15} =$ **17.** $\frac{12}{16} =$ **18.** $\frac{16}{24} =$

Find an equivalent fraction with the given denominator.

19. $\frac{2}{5} = \frac{\_\_}{15}$ **20.** $\frac{3}{4} = \frac{\_\_}{12}$ **21.** $\frac{2}{3} = \frac{\_\_}{12}$ **22.** $\frac{1}{4} = \frac{\_\_}{20}$

Compare each pair of fractions. Write >, <, or =.

23. $\frac{5}{6} \square \frac{1}{2}$ **24.** $\frac{2}{5} \square \frac{1}{2}$ **25.** $\frac{5}{8} \square \frac{2}{3}$ **26.** $\frac{9}{24} \square \frac{3}{8}$

UNIT 2 Adding and Subtracting Fractions

Real-Life Matters

Participating in a team sport often requires that you practice many days each week. For fall sports you join the track team. Your coach posts the following training schedule in the locker room:

Monday $1\frac{1}{2}$ hours

Tuesday $1\frac{3}{4}$ hours

Wednesday $\frac{3}{4}$ hours

Thursday $1\frac{1}{3}$ hours

Friday $1\frac{1}{2}$ hours

Real-Life Application

During one week you practice on Monday, Tuesday, and Thursday. How many hours did you practice?

____

____

The week before the state championship the coach wants you to practice for $4\frac{1}{4}$ hours. So far you have practiced on Monday and Tuesday. How many more hours of practice will you need?

____

____

One week you practice on Tuesday, Wednesday, and Friday. The next week you practice on Monday, Tuesday, and Thursday. During which week did you practice more? By how many hours?

____

____

The coach requires that you practice at least $3\frac{3}{4}$ hours each week. On which days would you choose to practice?

____

____

Overview • Lessons 9–11

Adding Fractions

Compare the two graham crackers. One is cut into four equal parts. Each part is called a fourth. The other is cut into two equal halves. Notice that two fourths are the same as one half.

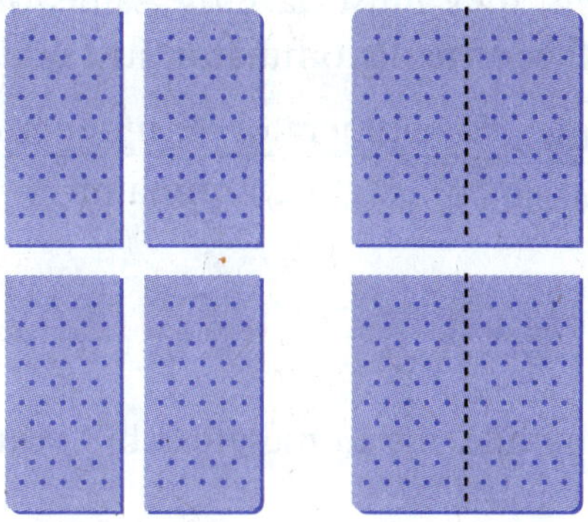

Another way of saying this is:

$$\frac{1}{4} + \frac{1}{4} = \frac{2}{4} = \frac{1}{2}$$

When you add the two **like fractions,** fractions with the same denominator, you add the numerators. The denominator stays the same. As always, simplify the answer, if necessary.

When you add two **unlike fractions,** fractions whose denominators are different, you have to rename them so that all denominators are the same.

YOU KNOW

- How to find the least common denominator
- How to find equivalent fractions

YOU WILL LEARN

- How to add fractions with like and unlike denominators
- How to add mixed numbers

Remember the BASICS

Simplify the fractions. If you need to review these skills, turn to page 10.

1. $\frac{10}{12} = \frac{5}{6}$	**2.** $\frac{3}{6} =$	**3.** $\frac{8}{12} =$	**4.** $\frac{12}{18} =$
5. $\frac{9}{12} =$	**6.** $\frac{15}{20} =$	**7.** $\frac{21}{24} =$	**8.** $\frac{24}{32} =$

Write an equivalent fraction.

9. $\frac{1}{3} = \frac{2}{6}$	**10.** $\frac{2}{5} =$	**11.** $\frac{1}{4} =$	**12.** $\frac{2}{5} =$
13. $\frac{7}{8} =$	**14.** $\frac{2}{5} =$	**15.** $\frac{1}{9} =$	**16.** $\frac{7}{10} =$

LESSON 9 Adding with Like Denominators

Before you can add fractions, they must have the same, or common, denominators. If the fractions already have the same denominator, just add the numerators.

$$\frac{\text{numerator}}{\text{denominator}} + \frac{\text{numerator}}{\text{denominator}} = \frac{\text{numerator} + \text{numerator}}{\text{denominator}}$$

$$\frac{2}{6} + \frac{3}{6} = \frac{5}{6}$$

When you add fractions, you add the numerators but you do not add the denominators.

After you add, you must check to make sure that the fraction is in simplest form.

Example

Add. $\frac{2}{5} + \frac{1}{5}$

STEP 1 If both fractions have the same denominator, add the numerators.

$$\frac{2 + 1}{5} = \frac{3}{5}$$

STEP 2 If the answer is an improper fraction, rename it as a mixed number.
In this case, $\frac{3}{5}$ is a proper fraction, so there is no need to rename the fraction.

STEP 3 Simplify the fraction.
The fraction $\frac{3}{5}$ is already in simplest form.

$$\frac{2}{5} + \frac{1}{5} = \frac{3}{5}$$

ON YOUR OWN

Julio practiced his trumpet $\frac{3}{4}$ hours yesterday and $\frac{3}{4}$ hours today. How long did he practice in all?

Practice

Fractions that are answers must be in their simplest form.

Building Skills

Add.

1. $\frac{1}{8} + \frac{5}{8} =$

$\frac{1+5}{8} = \frac{6}{8} = \frac{3}{4}$

2. $\frac{1}{7} + \frac{1}{7} =$

3. $\frac{3}{20} + \frac{7}{20} =$

4. $\frac{1}{4} + \frac{1}{4} =$

5. $\frac{1}{10} + \frac{7}{10} =$

6. $\frac{4}{15} + \frac{8}{15} =$

7. $\frac{7}{12} + \frac{11}{12} =$

8. $\frac{4}{9} + \frac{5}{9} =$

9. $\frac{13}{16} + \frac{7}{16} =$

Problem Solving

Solve.

10. At the community center, Maureen answered $\frac{1}{5}$ of the phone calls. Donna answered $\frac{3}{5}$ of the phone calls. What part of the phone calls did they answer in all?

$\frac{1}{5} + \frac{3}{5} = \frac{1+3}{5} = \frac{4}{5}$

11. Benny read $\frac{2}{5}$ of his book last night. He read another $\frac{2}{5}$ this morning. What part of the book has he read so far?

12. Jessica gave $\frac{3}{6}$ of last year's school clothes to charity and $\frac{1}{6}$ to her cousin. What part of her clothing did she give away?

13. If $\frac{3}{8}$ of a class is in the school chorus and $\frac{1}{8}$ is in the school band, what part of the class is involved in either chorus or band?

14. In history class, $\frac{3}{5}$ of your grade is based on test scores and $\frac{1}{5}$ on class participation. How much of your total grade is this?

15. The treasurer reports that $\frac{3}{10}$ of your class paid their class dues at the start of the school year. Another $\frac{2}{10}$ paid dues after the winter break. How many of the students paid their class dues?

LESSON 10 Adding with Unlike Denominators

When you add fractions, their denominators must be the same. But what happens when you need to add fractions that have different denominators? You have to rename the fractions as equivalent fractions so that all fractions have the same denominator. Then you add the numerators. Remember, equivalent fractions are fractions that name the same value.

Example

Add. $\frac{1}{4} + \frac{1}{3}$

STEP 1 **Find the least common denominator (LCD).**

4: 4, 8, **12,** 16, 20

3: 3, 6, 9, **12,** 15

The LCD of 3 and 4 is 12.

STEP 2 **Write equivalent fractions with the LCD.**
Remember that to get the equivalent fraction you must multiply the numerator and denominator by the same number.

$$\frac{1}{4} \times \frac{3}{3} = \frac{3}{12}$$
$$\frac{1}{3} \times \frac{4}{4} = \frac{4}{12}$$

STEP 3 **Add the numerators.**

$$\frac{3 + 4}{12} = \frac{7}{12}$$

STEP 4 **If necessary, rewrite as a mixed number and/or simplify the answer.**
In this case neither step is necessary, because $\frac{7}{12}$ is both a proper fraction and in simplest form.

$$\frac{1}{4} + \frac{1}{3} = \frac{7}{12}$$

ON YOUR OWN

Ramon jogged for $\frac{2}{3}$ hours. Crystal jogged for $\frac{1}{2}$ an hour. How long did they both jog?

Practice

Find the LCD and then add.

Building Skills

Add.

1. $\frac{1}{4} + \frac{2}{3} =$ $\frac{1}{4} \times \frac{3}{3} = \frac{3}{12}$ $\frac{2}{3} \times \frac{4}{4} = \frac{8}{12}$ $\frac{8 + 3}{12} = \frac{11}{12}$

2. $\frac{1}{2} + \frac{3}{5} =$

3. $\frac{3}{8} + \frac{1}{6} =$

4. $\frac{1}{9} + \frac{5}{6} =$

5. $\frac{2}{3} + \frac{5}{6} =$

6. $\frac{4}{5} + \frac{1}{2} =$

7. $\frac{7}{8} + \frac{5}{6} =$

8. $\frac{3}{4} + \frac{4}{5} =$

9. $\frac{9}{10} + \frac{1}{4} =$

Problem Solving

Solve.

10. Alvaro practiced for $\frac{1}{2}$ an hour yesterday and $\frac{1}{4}$ of an hour today. How long did he practice altogether?

$\frac{1}{2} \times \frac{2}{2} = \frac{2}{4}; \frac{1}{4} \times \frac{1}{1} = \frac{1}{4}; \frac{2}{4} + \frac{1}{4} = \frac{3}{4}$

11. Pam worked on her car for $\frac{3}{4}$ of an hour on Saturday and for $\frac{5}{6}$ of an hour on Sunday. How much time did she spend on her car over the weekend?

12. Drayton's video project filled $\frac{2}{8}$ of a recordable CD. Rob's video filled $\frac{1}{3}$ of a disc. How much disc space do both projects use?

13. Ann spent $\frac{2}{3}$ of an hour fixing her bike and then $\frac{5}{6}$ of an hour riding the bike. How many hours did she spend altogether?

14. Terry spent $\frac{1}{3}$ of his paycheck on a haircut and $\frac{2}{7}$ on school lunches for the week. What portion of his earnings did he spend that week?

15. Yeng spent $\frac{2}{8}$ of her day updating her Web site and $\frac{3}{6}$ of that day at her part-time job. How much of the day did she spend on those two activities?

LESSON 11 Adding Mixed Numbers

On a typical afternoon at your job, you work for $2\frac{1}{2}$ hours, you take a break, and then you work for another $1\frac{3}{4}$ hours. If you wanted the total number of hours you worked, you would add mixed numbers.

When you add mixed numbers, you first add the whole numbers. Then you add the fractions. Remember that when you add any fractions, the denominators must be the same.

Example

Add. $2\frac{3}{8} + 3\frac{1}{4}$

STEP 1 **Find the least common denominator (LCD) of the fractions.**
List the multiples of 4 and 8.
4: 4, 8, 12, 16
8: 8, 16, 24, 32
The LCD of 4 and 8 is 8.

STEP 2 **Write equivalent fractions using the LCD.**

$$\frac{1}{4} \times \frac{2}{2} = \frac{2}{8}$$

STEP 3 **Add the fractions.**

$$\frac{2}{8} + \frac{3}{8} = \frac{5}{8}$$

STEP 4 **Add the whole numbers.**
$2 + 3 = 5$

STEP 5 **Combine the whole number part and the fraction, and simplify the fraction if necessary.**
The fraction $5\frac{5}{8}$ is in simplest form.

$$2\frac{3}{8} + 3\frac{1}{4} = 5\frac{5}{8}$$

ON YOUR OWN

Sara has collected $3\frac{3}{4}$ pounds of newspaper for recycling. Henry has collected $4\frac{1}{2}$ pounds. How much do they have together?

Practice

The denominators of the fractions must be the same before you add.

Building Skills

Add.

1. $2\frac{1}{6} + 2\frac{2}{3} =$

$\frac{1}{6} + \frac{2}{3} = \frac{1}{6} + \frac{4}{6} = \frac{5}{6}$

$2 + 2 = 4$

$4 + \frac{5}{6} = 4\frac{5}{6}$

2. $5\frac{2}{5} + 2\frac{3}{10} =$

3. $1\frac{1}{3} + 2\frac{1}{4} =$

4. $3\frac{5}{8} + 2\frac{1}{6} =$

5. $3\frac{1}{2} + 4\frac{2}{5} =$

6. $6\frac{2}{3} + 2\frac{3}{5} =$

7. $7\frac{4}{9} + 2\frac{1}{6} =$

8. $2\frac{4}{5} + 3\frac{1}{6} =$

9. $5\frac{7}{10} + 2\frac{3}{4} =$

Problem Solving

Solve.

10. Jake biked $4\frac{5}{8}$ miles from the cottage to the beach and another $2\frac{1}{2}$ miles to work. How many total miles did he ride?

$\frac{5}{8} + \frac{1}{2} = \frac{5}{8} + \frac{4}{8} = \frac{9}{8}$

$4 + 2 = 6$

$6 + \frac{9}{8} = 6\frac{9}{8} = 7\frac{1}{8}$

11. Aki played a computer game for $1\frac{5}{6}$ hours yesterday and played for $1\frac{3}{4}$ hours today. How long did she play in all?

12. Tina ran for $15\frac{3}{5}$ minutes one day and $17\frac{9}{10}$ minutes another day. How long did she run in all?

13. Sol left his house and spent $2\frac{1}{2}$ hours at the movies and $1\frac{3}{4}$ hours at the gym. How long was he gone?

14. The first act of the play took $1\frac{2}{3}$ hours. The second act lasted $2\frac{1}{4}$ hours. How long was the play?

15. You volunteered $3\frac{2}{5}$ hours last week and $12\frac{4}{6}$ hours this week. How many hours have you volunteered?

TEST-TAKING STRATEGY

Work Backwards

Sometimes working backwards is the best way to solve a problem.

Example

Santos sold $3\frac{3}{4}$ pounds of buffalo wings to Mrs. Gallo. Then he sold $5\frac{1}{2}$ pounds of buffalo wings to Mr. Chen. He has $1\frac{5}{8}$ pounds of buffalo wings left. How many pounds of buffalo wings did Santos start with?

STEP 1 Decide what problem you need to solve.
How many pounds did Santos start with?

STEP 2 List what you know.
$3\frac{3}{4}$ pounds sold; $5\frac{1}{2}$ pounds sold; $1\frac{5}{8}$ pounds left

STEP 3 Work backwards to find the answer.
When you work backwards use the opposite operations.
When Santos sold buffalo wings, he was subtracting from the original amount. The opposite of subtraction is addition.

Buffalo wings Santos has left (lb) →	$1\frac{5}{8}$	$= 1\frac{5}{8}$
Buffalo wings sold to Mr. Chen (lb)	$5\frac{1}{2}$	$= 5\frac{4}{8}$
Buffalo wings sold to Mrs. Gallo (lb) →	$+3\frac{3}{4}$	$= +3\frac{6}{8}$
Buffalo wings Santos started with (lb) →	$9\frac{15}{8}$	$= 10\frac{7}{8}$

Santos started with $10\frac{7}{8}$ lb of buffalo wings.

TRY IT OUT

Circle the correct answer.

Beth filled her car's gas tank on Friday. She used $5\frac{1}{2}$ gallons of gas on the weekend. She used $6\frac{3}{5}$ gallons commuting to work all week. Now she has $2\frac{9}{10}$ gallons of gas left in her car. How much gasoline does her car's gas tank hold?

A. 2 gallons **B.** 13 gallons **C.** $14\frac{1}{10}$ gallons **D.** 15 gallons

Option D is correct. When you work backwards and add $2\frac{9}{10} + 6\frac{3}{5} + 5\frac{1}{2}$, the sum is 15.

Overview • Lessons 12–14

Subtracting Fractions

You and your friend take the school bus from your home to school each day. The distance from your house to the school is $9\frac{3}{4}$ miles. After the bus travels $2\frac{1}{2}$ miles it picks up another friend. How many miles do you have to go to reach the school? To find the remaining distance to the school you subtract $9\frac{3}{4} - 2\frac{1}{2}$.

You can use the fraction skills you already know to subtract fractions. When you're subtracting fractions, you may have to find the LCD and equivalent fractions just as you did in adding fractions.

Subtracting fractions includes

- Subtracting fractions from mixed numbers
- Subtracting fractions from whole numbers
- Subtracting fractions with different denominators
- Subtracting fractions with like denominators

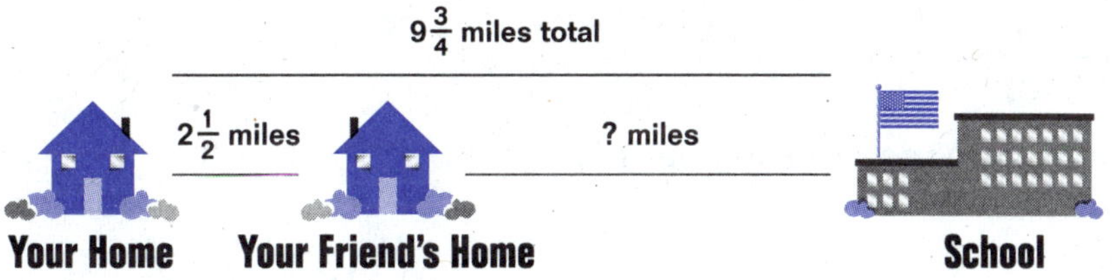

YOU KNOW

- How to subtract whole numbers
- How to find a common denominator
- How to add fractions
- How to change mixed numbers to improper fractions

YOU WILL LEARN

- How to subtract fractions with different denominators
- How to subtract fractions by renaming mixed numbers

Remember the BASICS

Change each mixed number to an improper fraction.

1. $3\frac{2}{3} = \frac{11}{3}$
2. $5\frac{4}{5} =$
3. $7\frac{1}{8} =$
4. $4\frac{3}{4} =$

Find an equivalent fraction for each.

5. $\frac{2}{9} = \frac{4}{18}$
6. $\frac{1}{6} =$
7. $\frac{4}{5} =$
8. $\frac{3}{4} =$

Simplify each fraction.

9. $\frac{12}{15} = \frac{4}{5}$
10. $\frac{14}{16} =$
11. $\frac{18}{24} =$
12. $\frac{20}{25} =$
13. $\frac{6}{36} =$
14. $\frac{24}{28} =$
15. $\frac{16}{24} =$
16. $\frac{18}{21} =$

LESSON 12 Subtracting Fractions with Like Denominators

As with adding fractions, when you subtract fractions, you need to make sure they have a common denominator. If the fractions already have the same denominator, just subtract the numerators.

$$\frac{5}{6} - \frac{3}{6} = \frac{2}{6}$$

The basic idea is this:

$$\frac{\text{numerator}}{\text{denominator}} - \frac{\text{numerator}}{\text{denominator}} = \frac{\text{numerator} - \text{numerator}}{\text{denominator}}$$

When you subtract fractions, you subtract the numerators but you do not subtract the denominators.

After you subtract, you must check to make sure that the fraction is in simplest form.

Example

Subtract. $\frac{9}{10} - \frac{3}{10}$

STEP 1 **If both fractions have the same denominator, subtract the numerators.**

$$\frac{9-3}{10} = \frac{6}{10}$$

STEP 2 **If the result is an improper fraction, change it to a mixed number.**
In this case, $\frac{6}{10}$ is a proper fraction, so there is no need to rename it as a mixed number.

STEP 3 **Simplify the fraction.**
$\frac{6}{10}$ is not in simplest form. Divide the numerator and denominator by 2.

$$\frac{6}{10} \div \frac{2}{2} = \frac{3}{5}$$

$$\frac{9}{10} - \frac{3}{10} = \frac{6}{10} = \frac{3}{5}$$

ON YOUR OWN

After lunch, Jana had $\frac{7}{8}$ of a pizza left. She gave $\frac{3}{8}$ of the pizza to her sister. What part of the pizza is left?

Practice

Building Skills

Subtract.

1. $\frac{5}{6} - \frac{1}{6} =$

$\frac{5-1}{6} = \frac{4}{6} = \frac{2}{3}$

2. $\frac{7}{8} - \frac{5}{8} =$

3. $\frac{4}{4} - \frac{1}{4} =$

4. $\frac{3}{5} - \frac{1}{5} =$

5. $\frac{8}{9} - \frac{5}{9} =$

6. $\frac{10}{10} - \frac{1}{4} =$

7. $\frac{11}{12} - \frac{7}{12} =$

8. $\frac{13}{16} - \frac{5}{16} =$

9. $\frac{20}{20} - \frac{13}{20} =$

Problem Solving

Solve.

10. Lorenzo lives $\frac{8}{10}$ of a mile from school. Angelo lives $\frac{4}{10}$ of a mile from school. How much farther does Lorenzo live from the school than Angelo?

$\frac{8-4}{10} = \frac{4}{10} = \frac{2}{5}$

11. Jesse read $\frac{1}{12}$ of a book. What fraction of the book does he have left to read?

12. Shandra had $\frac{5}{8}$ of a cup of oil. She used $\frac{3}{8}$ of a cup of oil in a recipe. How much oil does Shandra have left?

13. Malik has to weed $\frac{11}{12}$ of the garden in the backyard. He weeded $\frac{5}{12}$ of the garden on Saturday. What fraction of the garden does he have left to weed on Sunday?

14. Rachel bought an eight-slice pizza. She ate $\frac{1}{8}$ of the pizza. How much was left?

15. The sporting goods store sells exercise mats that are $\frac{7}{8}$ of an inch thick. Another store sells mats that are $\frac{5}{8}$ of an inch thick. How much thicker are the mats sold by the first store?

LESSON 13 Subtracting Fractions with Unlike Denominators

When you subtract fractions, their denominators must be the same. But what happens when you need to subtract fractions that have different denominators? You have to make sure that the fractions have the same denominator. You will need to find equivalent fractions. Equivalent fractions are fractions that name the same value. Then you simply subtract the numerators.

Example

Subtract. $\frac{2}{3} - \frac{1}{2}$

STEP 1 **Find the least common denominator (LCD).**
Find the LCD by listing the multiples of each denominator.
3: 3, 6, 9, 12
2: 2, 4, 6, 8, 10
The LCD of 2 and 3 is 6.

STEP 2 **Write equivalent fractions with the LCD.**
Remember, that to get the equivalent fraction, you must multiply the numerator and denominator by the same number.

$$\frac{2}{3} \times \frac{2}{2} = \frac{4}{6}$$
$$\frac{1}{2} \times \frac{3}{3} = \frac{3}{6}$$

STEP 3 **Subtract the numerators and keep the denominator the same.**

$$\frac{4-3}{6} = \frac{1}{6}$$

STEP 4 **Simplify the fraction if necessary.**
In this case this step is not necessary, because $\frac{1}{6}$ is in simplest form.

$$\frac{2}{3} - \frac{1}{2} = \frac{1}{6}$$

ON YOUR OWN

Shannon played a video game for $\frac{3}{4}$ of an hour. Lori played the same game for $\frac{2}{3}$ of an hour. How much longer did Shannon play?

Practice

Be sure your answer is in its simplest form.

Building Skills

Subtract.

1. $\frac{7}{10} - \frac{1}{2} =$

The LCD is 10.

$\frac{7}{10} \times \frac{1}{1} = \frac{7}{10}; \frac{1}{2} \times \frac{5}{5} = \frac{5}{10}$

$\frac{7-5}{10} = \frac{2}{10} = \frac{1}{5}$

2. $\frac{2}{3} - \frac{1}{6} =$

3. $\frac{4}{5} - \frac{1}{10} =$

4. $\frac{1}{3} - \frac{1}{4} =$

5. $\frac{5}{9} - \frac{1}{3} =$

6. $\frac{7}{8} - \frac{3}{4} =$

7. $\frac{11}{12} - \frac{3}{8} =$

8. $\frac{15}{16} - \frac{3}{4} =$

9. $\frac{5}{9} - \frac{1}{6} =$

Problem Solving

Solve.

10. You walk $\frac{9}{10}$ miles from your home to the center of town. On the way back, you stop at a store that is $\frac{1}{3}$ miles from town center. How far is the store from your home?

$\frac{9}{10} - \frac{1}{3}$; LCD is 30.

$\frac{9}{10} \times \frac{3}{3} = \frac{27}{30}; \frac{1}{3} \times \frac{10}{10} = \frac{10}{30}$

$\frac{27-10}{30} = \frac{17}{30}$

11. Larissa ran $\frac{1}{5}$ miles on Thursday and $\frac{7}{10}$ miles on Friday. How much farther did Larissa run on Friday than on Thursday?

12. Deion needed $\frac{7}{8}$ of a yard of material to make a banner. If he has $\frac{5}{6}$ of a yard, how much more does he need?

13. Anna ran $\frac{9}{10}$ of a mile. Lucia ran $\frac{3}{4}$ of a mile. How much farther did Anna run?

LESSON 14 Subtracting Mixed Numbers

One day at your summer job, you need to take time off for a doctor's appointment. Ordinarily, your workday is $8\frac{1}{2}$ hours long, but you are away for $1\frac{1}{4}$ hours. How long did you end up working that day?

In one way, subtracting mixed numbers is like adding mixed numbers: when you subtract, you subtract the whole numbers and fractions separately.

But sometimes you cannot subtract fractions as easily as you can add them. That is when you have to **regroup** one of the mixed numbers.

Example

Subtract. $8\frac{1}{2} - 1\frac{1}{4}$

STEP 1 Find the least common denominator (LCD) of the fractions.
List the multiples of 2 and 4.
2: 2, 4, 6, 8, 10
4: 4, 8, 12, 16
The LCD of 2 and 4 is 4.

STEP 2 Write equivalent fractions using the LCD.

$\frac{1}{2} \times \frac{2}{2} = \frac{2}{4}$

$\frac{1}{4} \times \frac{1}{1} = \frac{1}{4}$

STEP 3 If necessary, regroup one of the whole numbers as a fraction. Add it to the fraction that is there already.
Since you can subtract $\frac{1}{4}$ from $\frac{2}{4}$, you do not need to rename any other part of the mixed number.

$\frac{2}{4} - \frac{1}{4} = \frac{1}{4}$

STEP 4 Subtract the whole numbers and the fractions.
$8 - 1 = 7$

STEP 5 Combine the new whole number and the new fraction to make a new mixed number or proper fraction. Simplify if necessary.
The difference is $7\frac{1}{4}$. In this example, the difference is already in simplest form.

$8\frac{1}{2} - 1\frac{1}{4} = 7\frac{1}{4}$

$7 + \frac{1}{4} = 7\frac{1}{4}$.

ON YOUR OWN

Jamie caught a fish that weighs $2\frac{3}{4}$ pounds. Her uncle caught a fish that weighs $3\frac{1}{2}$ pounds. How many more pounds does Jamie's uncle's fish weigh?

Practice

Building Skills

Subtract.

1. $3\frac{1}{3} - 1\frac{1}{2} =$

$3\frac{1}{3} \times \frac{2}{2} = 3\frac{2}{6}$ $1\frac{1}{2} \times \frac{3}{3} = 1\frac{3}{6}$

$3\frac{2}{6} = 2 + \frac{6}{6} + \frac{2}{6} = 2\frac{8}{6}$

$2\frac{8}{6} - 1\frac{3}{6} = 1\frac{5}{6}$

2. $4\frac{5}{8} - 2\frac{1}{4} =$

3. $5\frac{2}{3} - 1\frac{1}{2} =$

4. $4\frac{3}{4} - 2\frac{2}{3} =$

5. $3\frac{1}{4} - 1\frac{1}{2} =$

6. $6\frac{3}{8} - 2\frac{7}{8} =$

7. $8\frac{2}{5} - 1\frac{1}{3} =$

8. $3\frac{1}{6} - 1\frac{11}{12} =$

9. $12\frac{3}{8} - 6\frac{5}{6} =$

Problem Solving

Solve.

10. Mary Ellen swam for $12\frac{2}{3}$ minutes yesterday. The day before she swam for only $9\frac{1}{2}$ minutes. How much longer did she swim the second day?

$12\frac{2}{3} - 9\frac{1}{2} = 3\frac{1}{6}$

11. Ms. Gutierrez had $2\frac{1}{3}$ pounds of chocolate for a party. Her guests ate $1\frac{1}{4}$ pounds. How many pounds of chocolate were left?

12. Renee used $2\frac{3}{4}$ rolls of film at the party and $4\frac{1}{2}$ rolls of film at the graduation ceremony. How many more rolls of film did she use at the graduation?

13. Mariana filled $2\frac{1}{3}$ bins for recycling. Eric filled $1\frac{1}{4}$ bins. How much more recycling material did Mariana have?

14. Claudio swam $3\frac{5}{8}$ lengths of the pool. Derrick swam $1\frac{1}{4}$ lengths of the pool fewer than Claudio did. How many lengths of the pool did Derrick swim?

15. Melissa painted $4\frac{5}{6}$ square feet of the wall. Althea painted $1\frac{3}{4}$ square feet less than Melissa did. How many square feet of the wall did Althea paint?

TEST-TAKING STRATEGY

Guess and Check

You can guess an answer to a test question about subtracting fractions and then check your answer to see if it is correct. If your answer is not correct, guess and check again.

Example

A batch of trail mix contains $\frac{5}{8}$ quart of nuts. The mix contains $\frac{1}{8}$ quart more of peanuts than walnuts. How many quarts of peanuts are in the trail mix?

STEP 1 Guess two fractions that you think have a difference of $\frac{1}{8}$ and a sum of $\frac{5}{8}$.
In this problem, remember the total amount of nuts is $\frac{5}{8}$, the difference between the amount of peanuts and the amount of walnuts is $\frac{1}{8}$. Therefore, you need to find two fractions that add up to $\frac{5}{8}$, yet after you subtract, have a difference of $\frac{1}{8}$.

Guess: $\frac{2}{8}$ and $\frac{1}{8}$

Check: $\frac{2}{8} - \frac{1}{8} = \frac{1}{8} \leftarrow$ The difference is $\frac{1}{8}$.

$\frac{2}{8} + \frac{1}{8} = \frac{3}{8} \leftarrow$ The sum is too low.

STEP 2 Try two more fractions that have a difference of $\frac{1}{8}$. Use fractions that you think have a sum greater than the fractions you tried in your first guess.

Guess: $\frac{4}{8}$ and $\frac{3}{8}$

Check: $\frac{4}{8} - \frac{3}{8} = \frac{1}{8} \leftarrow$ The difference is $\frac{1}{8}$.

$\frac{4}{8} + \frac{3}{8} = \frac{7}{8} \leftarrow$ The sum is too high.

STEP 3 Now try two fractions that are between the fractions you tried in your first two guesses.

Guess: $\frac{3}{8}$ and $\frac{2}{8}$

Check: $\frac{3}{8} - \frac{2}{8} = \frac{1}{8} \leftarrow$ The difference is $\frac{1}{8}$.

$\frac{3}{8} + \frac{2}{8} = \frac{5}{8} \leftarrow$ The sum is $\frac{5}{8}$.

The trail mix contains $\frac{3}{8}$ quart of peanuts.

TRY IT OUT

Myra used $\frac{11}{12}$ of a yard of ribbon to wrap a package. She used $\frac{5}{12}$ of a yard more yellow ribbon than purple ribbon. How many yards of purple ribbon did Myra use?

Circle the correct answer.

A. $\frac{1}{12}$ yard B. $\frac{3}{12}$ yard C. $\frac{5}{12}$ yard D. $\frac{8}{12}$ yard

Option B is correct. $\frac{8}{12} - \frac{3}{12} = \frac{5}{12}$ and $\frac{8}{12} + \frac{3}{12} = \frac{11}{12}$.

UNIT 2 Review

Add. Simplify if necessary.

1. $\frac{3}{8} + \frac{1}{8} =$

2. $\frac{2}{3} + \frac{1}{3} =$

3. $\frac{3}{10} + \frac{3}{10} =$

4. $\frac{5}{12} + \frac{7}{12} =$

Subtract. Simplify if necessary.

5. $\frac{9}{10} - \frac{3}{10} =$

6. $\frac{5}{6} - \frac{1}{6} =$

7. $\frac{5}{12} - \frac{1}{12} =$

8. $\frac{7}{8} - \frac{1}{8} =$

Find the LCD and add. Simplify if necessary.

9. $\frac{1}{2} + \frac{1}{4} =$

10. $\frac{2}{5} + \frac{3}{10} =$

11. $\frac{3}{4} + \frac{5}{6} =$

12. $\frac{4}{5} + \frac{2}{3} =$

Find the LCD and subtract. Simplify if necessary.

13. $\frac{1}{2} - \frac{1}{4} =$

14. $\frac{5}{8} - \frac{1}{4} =$

15. $\frac{4}{5} - \frac{3}{4} =$

16. $\frac{11}{12} - \frac{3}{8} =$

Add. Simplify if necessary.

17. $3\frac{1}{2} + 4\frac{1}{4} =$

18. $2\frac{2}{5} + 4\frac{1}{2} =$

19. $5\frac{7}{8} + 2\frac{3}{4} =$

Subtract. Simplify if necessary.

20. $3\frac{3}{4} - 2\frac{1}{2} =$

21. $4\frac{5}{6} - 1\frac{1}{5} =$

22. $3\frac{1}{3} - 1\frac{1}{2} =$

Solve.

23. Sam used $3\frac{5}{6}$ gallons of paint to paint his room. He started with $6\frac{1}{8}$ gallons of paint. How much paint did he have left when he was finished?

24. One juice bottle contains $6\frac{3}{5}$ cups of juice. A second bottle contains $1\frac{9}{10}$ cups of juice. If you combine the juice from both bottles, how much juice will you have?

UNIT 3 Multiplying and Dividing Fractions

Real-Life Matters

A magazine article on people and their pets reports that of 1,000 people surveyed, $\frac{3}{4}$ own a dog. To find the actual number of people owning a dog, you multiply $1{,}000 \times \frac{3}{4}$. You find out that 750 of the people responding to the survey own a dog.

Real-Life Application

The same report showed that $\frac{2}{3}$ of the people liked short-haired dogs. Out of 1,000 people, how many people like short-haired dogs?

____

____

When you multiply by a fraction, you are finding part of something.

The same study showed that $\frac{1}{3}$ of the people asked had at least 2 dogs. How many people had at least 2 dogs?

____

____

In the example above, you are finding the *part* of all the people responding. You multiply the total number of people by each fraction to find the part of all people who responded.

When you divide by fractions, a whole number will get larger.

Next to the article is an advertisement for dog treats. The bulk version of the treats is a $2\frac{1}{2}$-pound pack containing $\frac{1}{2}$-pound bags. How many small bags of treats are in the bulk package?

____

____

You divide to find how many parts are in the total.

Overview • Lessons 15–16

Multiplying Fractions

You may have noticed that cooking uses a lot of fractions. Sometimes you may not want to make the full amount called for in a recipe. How would you go about reducing a recipe?

Sylvia wants to try out her grandmother's lasagne recipe, which serves eight people. Sylvia's family is small—just her mother, father, and brother—so she wants to make half the recipe. The original recipe calls for $\frac{1}{2}$ pound of ground beef. Is there more than one way to cut this amount in half?

Multiplying fractions is similar to multiplying whole numbers. You apply the same rules of multiplication to each part of the fraction.

YOU KNOW

- How to multiply whole numbers
- How to simplify fractions
- How to change a mixed number to an improper fraction

YOU WILL LEARN

- How to multiply fractions
- How to multiply mixed numbers

Remember the BASICS

Write the fraction in simplest form. Example: $\frac{2}{6} \div \frac{2}{2} = \frac{1}{3}$

1. $\frac{16}{20} =$
2. $\frac{18}{27} =$
3. $\frac{40}{50} =$
4. $\frac{20}{25} =$
5. $\frac{9}{15} =$
6. $\frac{15}{35} =$
7. $\frac{21}{35} =$
8. $\frac{6}{18} =$

Write each mixed number as an improper fraction. Example: $5\frac{1}{2} = \frac{2 \times 5 + 1}{2} = \frac{11}{2}$

9. $3\frac{1}{3} =$
10. $4\frac{3}{4} =$
11. $3\frac{2}{5} =$
12. $5\frac{5}{8} =$

LESSON 15 Multiplying Fractions

Suppose you have $\frac{1}{2}$ a dollar and your friend asks you for $\frac{1}{2}$ of your money. You would then have $\frac{1}{2}$ of a $\frac{1}{2}$ dollar, which is the same as 25 cents, or a quarter ($\frac{1}{4}$ of a dollar). You can write: $\frac{1}{2} \times \frac{1}{2} = \frac{1}{4}$.

When you multiply fractions, you multiply the numerators by each other and the denominators by each other. Remember to simplify your answer if necessary.

$$\frac{7}{8} \times \frac{3}{4} = \frac{7 \times 3}{8 \times 4} = \frac{21}{32}$$

Example

Multiply. $\frac{7}{8} \times \frac{4}{5}$

STEP 1 **Multiply numerator by numerator and denominator by denominator.**

$$\frac{7 \times 4}{8 \times 5} = \frac{28}{40}$$

STEP 2 **Make sure the answer (the product) is in simplest form.** Remember, when you simplify a fraction, you look for a number that will divide evenly into both parts of the fraction. You can divide each part of the fraction by 4.

$$\frac{7}{8} \times \frac{4}{5} = \frac{28}{40} = \frac{7}{10}$$

$$\frac{28}{40} \div \frac{4}{4} = \frac{7}{10}$$

ON YOUR OWN

Helene painted $\frac{2}{3}$ of a wall white and $\frac{1}{2}$ of the wall red. What part of the wall was painted both red and white?

Practice

Building Skills

Multiply.

1. $\frac{5}{8} \times \frac{16}{25} =$

$\frac{5}{8} \times \frac{16}{25} = \frac{80}{200}$

$\frac{80}{100} \div \frac{40}{40} = \frac{2}{5}$

2. $\frac{3}{4} \times \frac{1}{3} =$

3. $\frac{2}{5} \times \frac{1}{6} =$

4. $\frac{2}{9} \times \frac{3}{5} =$

5. $\frac{5}{6} \times \frac{4}{5} =$

6. $\frac{8}{9} \times \frac{3}{4} =$

7. $\frac{15}{16} \times \frac{1}{10} =$

8. $\frac{6}{7} \times \frac{14}{15} =$

9. $\frac{9}{16} \times \frac{8}{15} =$

Problem Solving

Solve.

10. Ian's garden fills $\frac{2}{3}$ of his backyard. He plans to plant flowers in $\frac{1}{2}$ of the garden. How much of the garden will be for flowers?

$\frac{2}{3} \times \frac{1}{2} = \frac{2}{6} = \frac{1}{3}$

11. Andres has $\frac{1}{4}$ of a watermelon. He wants to give $\frac{1}{2}$ of this watermelon to his sister. What fraction of the watermelon is Andres going to give to his sister?

12. Rebecca's recipe calls for $\frac{4}{5}$ of a cup of flour. She plans to make $\frac{1}{4}$ of the recipe. How much flour will she use?

13. Joey ran $\frac{9}{10}$ of a mile. Juan ran $\frac{2}{3}$ as far as Joey. How far did Juan run?

14. The top of Elaine's desk measures 1 yard by $\frac{2}{3}$ of a yard. What is the area of the top of her desk? [Hint: area = length × width.]

15. A floor-cleaning solution is made using $\frac{1}{2}$ cup of ammonia for every 3 gallons of water. How much ammonia would you need if you were only making one gallon of floor cleaner?

LESSON 16 Multiplying Mixed Numbers

Multiplying mixed numbers is similar to what you just did to multiply fractions. To multiply mixed numbers you

- change the mixed numbers to improper fractions.
- multiply the fractions.
- rename the answer as a mixed number.

You can estimate your answer by rounding to the whole numbers and multiplying them. This gives you a number that is close to the actual product.

For example: $5\frac{1}{3} \times 2\frac{1}{2}$

Round the whole numbers: $5 \times 3 = 15$

The product should be close to 15.

Example

Multiply. $7\frac{1}{2} \times 3\frac{1}{4}$

STEP 1 Rename the mixed numbers as improper fractions.

$7\frac{1}{2} = \frac{15}{2} \quad 3\frac{1}{4} = \frac{13}{4}$

STEP 2 Multiply numerator by numerator, denominator by denominator.

$\frac{15 \times 13}{2 \times 4} = \frac{195}{8}$

STEP 3 Simplify the fraction and/or rename it as a mixed number.

$\frac{195}{8} = 24\frac{3}{8}$

STEP 4 Estimate the product to see if your result is reasonable.

$8 \times 3 = 24$

Your estimate is close to your answer.

$7\frac{1}{2} \times 3\frac{1}{4} = 24\frac{3}{8}$.

$7\frac{1}{2} \times 3\frac{1}{4} = 24\frac{3}{8}$

ON YOUR OWN

Jorge's room measures $12\frac{1}{2}$ feet by $9\frac{2}{5}$ feet. What is the area of his room? (Hint: area = length × width)

Practice

Building Skills

Multiply.

1. $3\frac{1}{3} \times 4\frac{1}{2} =$

$3\frac{1}{3} \times 4\frac{1}{2} = \frac{10}{3} \times \frac{9}{2} =$

$\frac{90}{6} = 15$

2. $1\frac{1}{4} \times 2\frac{2}{5} =$

3. $3\frac{1}{8} \times 4\frac{4}{5} =$

4. $5\frac{1}{4} \times 2\frac{4}{7} =$

5. $6\frac{1}{2} \times 3\frac{1}{5} =$

6. $3\frac{3}{4} \times 1\frac{1}{15} =$

7. $4\frac{3}{8} \times 4\frac{4}{7} =$

8. $3\frac{2}{3} \times 1\frac{1}{11} =$

9. $2\frac{13}{16} \times 4\frac{4}{9} =$

Problem Solving

Solve.

10. Jake's cubicle at his magazine internship measures $3\frac{1}{2}$ feet by $5\frac{1}{3}$ feet. What is the area of the cubicle?
(*Hint:* Area = length × width)

$3\frac{1}{2} = \frac{7}{2} \quad 5\frac{1}{3} = \frac{16}{3}$

$\frac{7}{2} \times \frac{16}{3} = \frac{112}{6} = 18\frac{4}{6} = 18\frac{2}{3}$

11. Rosa's formula uses $2\frac{1}{2}$ cups of water. If she wants to make $2\frac{1}{2}$ times the formula, how much water does she need?

12. Dana swims $5\frac{1}{2}$ laps in 2 minutes. Justine can swim $1\frac{1}{2}$ times as far in the same amount of time. How far will Justine swim in 2 minutes?

13. Terrell needs 6 pieces of cloth that are $4\frac{1}{2}$ feet long for decorations for the dance. How much material should he buy?

14. The size of a note card is $2\frac{3}{4}$ inches by $4\frac{1}{3}$ inches. What is the area of the card in square inches? (*Hint:* Area = length × width)

15. Leila is running a road race. Her average speed is $7\frac{1}{3}$ miles per hour. How long is the race if Leila finishes in $1\frac{1}{2}$ hours?

TEST–TAKING STRATEGY

Write an Equation or a Number Sentence

You can write an equation or a number sentence to answer test questions about multiplying fractions.

Example

Ben had 12 yards of material. He used $\frac{5}{8}$ of the material to make a school banner. How many yards of material did Ben use to make the banner?

STEP 1 Write an equation using words to model the problem.

yards of material × part used = material used

STEP 2 Write the equation using numbers.
Let n represent the number you are looking for.

yards of material		part used		material used
↓		↓		↓
12	×	$\frac{5}{8}$	=	n

STEP 3 Solve the equation.

$$12 \times \frac{5}{8} = n \rightarrow \frac{\overset{3}{\cancel{12}}}{1} \times \frac{5}{\underset{2}{\cancel{8}}} = n$$

$$\frac{15}{2} = n \qquad 7\frac{1}{2} = n$$

Ben used $7\frac{1}{2}$ yards of material to make the banner.

TRY IT OUT

Of the 30 students in the Computer Club, $\frac{5}{6}$ of them have laptop computers. How many students have laptop computers?

Circle the correct answer.

A. 6 **B.** 25 **C.** 30 **D.** 36

Option B is correct. $30 \times \frac{5}{6} = n$; $30 \times \frac{5}{6} = 25$.

Overview • Lessons 17–18

Dividing Fractions

You are building a doghouse. As part of the job, you need to cut a board that is $3\frac{3}{4}$ feet long into $\frac{3}{4}$-foot lengths. How many $\frac{3}{4}$-foot pieces can you get from the board? To find out you will divide $3\frac{3}{4}$ feet by $\frac{3}{4}$.

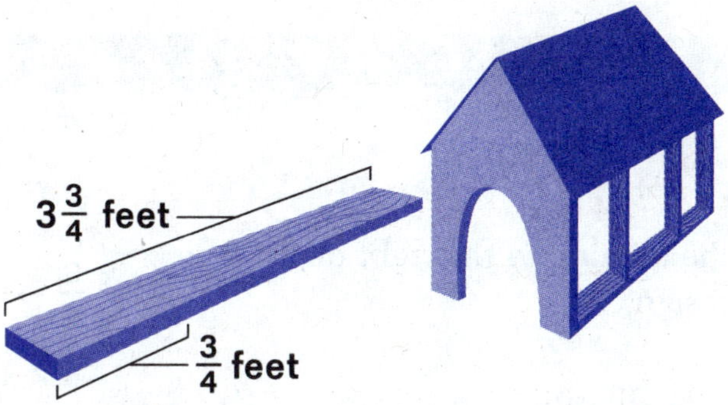

You know how to add, subtract, and multiply fractions. You also know how to simplify fractions and find equivalent fractions.

Dividing fractions involves using many of the same skills you learned in multiplying fractions.

YOU KNOW

- How to find the LCD
- How to divide whole numbers
- How to multiply fractions

YOU WILL LEARN

- How to divide fractions
- How to divide mixed numbers

Remember the BASICS

Multiply. Simplify your answer if necessary.

1. $\frac{1}{2} \times \frac{3}{4} = \frac{3}{8}$

2. $\frac{3}{5} \times \frac{1}{2} =$

3. $\frac{4}{9} \times \frac{2}{3} =$

4. $2\frac{5}{6} \times 4\frac{3}{8} =$

5. $6\frac{5}{12} \times 4\frac{3}{4} =$

6. $3\frac{3}{4} \times 3\frac{1}{2} =$

Simplify.

7. $\frac{3}{9} = \frac{3}{8} \div \frac{3}{3} = \frac{1}{3}$

8. $\frac{4}{10} =$

9. $\frac{18}{24} =$

10. $\frac{21}{49} =$

LESSON 17 Dividing Fractions

Divison is the opposite of multiplication. You can apply the skills you have learned for multiplying fractions to dividing fractions. When you divide fractions, you have to remember to **invert** the fraction to the right of the division sign before you multiply.

Example

Divide. $\frac{9}{10} \div \frac{3}{4}$

STEP 1 Invert the fraction to the right of the division sign.

$\frac{3}{4} \rightarrow \frac{4}{3}$

STEP 2 Change the division sign ($\div$) to a multiplication sign ($\times$).

$\frac{9}{10} \times \frac{4}{3}$

STEP 3 Multiply.

$\frac{9}{10} \times \frac{4}{3} = \frac{9 \times 4}{10 \times 3} = \frac{36}{30}$

STEP 4 Simplify the fraction and change to a mixed number if necessary.

$\frac{9}{10} \div \frac{3}{4} = 1\frac{1}{5}$

$\frac{36}{30} = 1\frac{6}{30} = 1\frac{1}{5}$

ON YOUR OWN

Jennie has a cake cut into $\frac{1}{6}$ pieces. She has $\frac{2}{3}$ of the cake left. How many slices is this?

Practice

Invert the fraction to the right of the division sign.

Building Skills

Divide.

1. $\frac{5}{6} \div \frac{1}{3} =$

$\frac{5}{6} \times \frac{3}{1} = \frac{15}{6} = 2\frac{3}{6} = 2\frac{1}{2}$

2. $\frac{3}{4} \div \frac{1}{2} =$

3. $\frac{9}{10} \div \frac{1}{4} =$

4. $\frac{7}{8} \div \frac{1}{3} =$

5. $\frac{4}{9} \div \frac{2}{3} =$

6. $\frac{5}{6} \div \frac{7}{8} =$

7. $\frac{15}{16} \div \frac{3}{16} =$

8. $\frac{21}{25} \div \frac{7}{10} =$

9. $\frac{4}{5} \div \frac{1}{6} =$

Problem Solving

Solve.

10. Lakesha has $\frac{3}{4}$ of a cup of walnuts to make cookies. If she plans to add $\frac{1}{3}$ of a cup per dozen cookies, how many dozen cookies can she make?

$\frac{3}{4} \div \frac{1}{3} = \frac{3}{4} \times \frac{3}{1} = \frac{9}{4} = 2\frac{1}{4}$

11. Anna is cutting pieces of wood for a birdhouse. If she has a board $\frac{3}{4}$ of a yard long and wants to cut pieces that are $\frac{1}{8}$ of a yard long, how many pieces will she get?

12. Franco has $\frac{5}{8}$ of a pie left. How many $\frac{1}{16}$ pieces can he cut from what he has now?

13. How many pieces of rope $\frac{1}{12}$ of a yard long can you cut from a piece of rope that measures $\frac{2}{3}$ of a yard?

LESSON 18 Dividing Mixed Numbers

When you divide mixed numbers, you must first change the mixed numbers to improper fractions. Then you divide the fractions the same way as you did in the last lesson. You must invert the fraction to the right of the division sign.

Example

Divide. $3\frac{1}{5} \div 1\frac{13}{15}$

STEP 1 Change the mixed numbers to improper fractions.

$\frac{16}{5} \div \frac{28}{15}$

STEP 2 Invert the fraction to the right of the division sign.

$\frac{28}{15} \rightarrow \frac{15}{28}$

STEP 3 Change the division sign (÷) to a multiplication sign (×).

$\frac{16}{5} \times \frac{15}{28} =$

STEP 4 Multiply.

$\frac{16}{5} \times \frac{15}{28} = \frac{15 \times 16}{5 \times 28} = \frac{240}{140}$

STEP 5 Simplify and change the answer to a mixed number if necessary.

$\frac{240}{140} = 1\frac{10}{14} = 1\frac{5}{7}$

$3\frac{1}{5} \div 1\frac{13}{15} = 1\frac{5}{7}$

ON YOUR OWN

Melissa rode her bike $23\frac{1}{3}$ miles in $2\frac{1}{2}$ hours. At that rate, how far did she ride in 1 hour?

Practice

Invert the fraction to the right of division sign.

Building Skills

Divide.

1. $3\frac{3}{4} \div 2\frac{1}{2} =$

$3\frac{3}{4} \div 2\frac{1}{2} = \frac{15}{4} \div \frac{5}{2}$

$\frac{15}{4} \times \frac{2}{5} = \frac{30}{20} = 1\frac{10}{20} = 1\frac{1}{2}$

2. $5\frac{1}{3} \div 1\frac{1}{6} =$

3. $1\frac{9}{10} \div 3\frac{1}{5} =$

4. $4\frac{1}{2} \div 3\frac{1}{3} =$

5. $3\frac{3}{4} \div 1\frac{2}{5} =$

6. $4\frac{1}{6} \div 1\frac{7}{8} =$

7. $1\frac{5}{12} \div 1\frac{5}{6} =$

8. $2\frac{2}{25} \div 1\frac{1}{10} =$

9. $8\frac{1}{3} \div 2\frac{1}{5} =$

Problem Solving

Solve.

10. Akiko has a recipe for a large omelet that requires $2\frac{3}{4}$ cups of milk. She wants to make an omelet that is $1\frac{1}{2}$ times smaller than the recipe. How many cups of milk does Akiko need for her omelet?

$2\frac{3}{4} \div 1\frac{1}{2} = \frac{11}{4} \div \frac{3}{2} =$

$\frac{11}{4} \times \frac{2}{3} = \frac{22}{12} = 1\frac{10}{12} = 1\frac{5}{6}$

11. Jorge has a pine board that is $12\frac{3}{8}$ feet long. He wants to cut it into $2\frac{1}{3}$-foot pieces. How many pieces, including the fraction of the leftover piece, will Jorge cut?

12. Martha is cutting rope into pieces for a craft project. The rope was $6\frac{1}{4}$ feet long, and there are $2\frac{1}{2}$ pieces. How long is each piece?

13. Mandy is using a $1\frac{1}{3}$-pint scoop to scoop water out of a large pot. The pot has 16 pints in it. How many scoops will it take to empty the pot?

TEST-TAKING STRATEGY

Choose an Operation

Sometimes you need to choose an operation to answer test questions about fractions.

Example

Cindy used $\frac{3}{4}$ of a cup of salsa to make tacos. She put $\frac{1}{8}$ of a cup of salsa on each taco. How many tacos did Cindy make?

STEP 1 Decide which operation to use to solve the problem.

- When you need to find the total in unequal groups, add.
- When you need to find how much is left, subtract.
- When you need to find the total in equal groups, multiply.
- When you need to find the number of equal groups or the number in each group, divide.

You need to find the number of equal groups to solve this problem, so you divide.

STEP 2 Use the operation to solve the problem.

$$\frac{3}{4} \div \frac{1}{8}$$

$$\frac{3}{4} \div \frac{1}{8} = \frac{3}{4} \times \frac{8}{1}$$

$$\frac{24}{4} = 6$$

Remember, when you divide by a fraction, you invert the fraction to the right of the division sign. Then multiply.

$$\frac{3}{4} \times \frac{8}{1} = \frac{24}{4} = 6$$

Cindy made 6 tacos.

TRY IT OUT

Mario cut a piece of wood into four equal pieces to make a picture frame. Each piece is $\frac{5}{6}$ of a foot long. What was the length of the wood before he cut it?

Circle the correct answer.

A. $3\frac{1}{3}$ **B.** $4\frac{5}{6}$ **C.** $20\frac{1}{4}$ **D.** $24\frac{1}{6}$

Option A is correct. In this problem, you need to find the total in equal groups, so you multiply. The length of the wood was $3\frac{1}{3}$ feet because $\frac{5}{6} \times 4 = 3\frac{1}{3}$.

Multiply. Simplify if necessary.

1. $\frac{2}{5} \times \frac{8}{9} =$

2. $\frac{5}{6} \times \frac{4}{5} =$

3. $\frac{3}{8} \times \frac{4}{15} =$

4. $\frac{21}{25} \times \frac{15}{28} =$

Divide. Simplify if necessary.

5. $\frac{3}{4} \div \frac{1}{4} =$

6. $\frac{9}{10} \div \frac{1}{5} =$

7. $\frac{7}{8} \div \frac{5}{6} =$

8. $\frac{15}{16} \div \frac{3}{8} =$

Multiply. Simplify if necessary.

9. $4\frac{4}{5} \times 4\frac{1}{6} =$

10. $2\frac{2}{5} \times 1\frac{3}{4} =$

Divide. Simplify if necessary.

11. $1\frac{3}{4} \div 1\frac{1}{4} =$

12. $3\frac{3}{5} \div 4\frac{1}{2} =$

13. $6\frac{1}{3} \div 1\frac{1}{9} =$

Solve.

14. The new park is $3\frac{1}{9}$ miles wide and $2\frac{4}{7}$ miles long. What is the total area of the park? (Hint: area = length × width)

15. Sallie has $2\frac{4}{10}$ ounces of scented lotion. She decides to put it into travel-size bottles that hold $1\frac{2}{5}$ ounces. How many bottles will Sallie use?

Post Test

Take this Post Test after you have completed this book. The Post Test will help you determine how far you have progressed in building your math skills.

Write a fraction for each sentence.

1. Nine out of twelve people attended the meeting. ____________________

2. José chose 10 out of 10 of the markers for his poster. ____________________

3. Ginny cut the pizza into 8 pieces and took 6 of them. ____________________

Write each fraction in simplest form.

4. $\frac{4}{12} =$

5. $\frac{6}{8} =$

6. $\frac{8}{16} =$

7. $\frac{12}{15} =$

Find the least common denominator (LCD).

8. $\frac{1}{3}$ and $\frac{7}{12}$

9. $\frac{2}{5}$ and $\frac{3}{11}$

10. $\frac{3}{4}$ and $\frac{7}{8}$

11. $\frac{5}{6}$ and $\frac{2}{5}$

Add. Simplify if necessary.

12. Lynn ate $\frac{1}{6}$ of the fruit salad. Her sister Leanne also ate $\frac{1}{6}$ of the fruit salad. How much of the fruit salad did they eat altogether?

13. $\frac{1}{3} + \frac{1}{6} =$

14. $4\frac{5}{6} + 1\frac{1}{2} =$

Subtract. Simplify if necessary.

15. $\frac{5}{6} - \frac{1}{6} =$

16. Calvin had $\frac{3}{4}$ of a bottle of orange juice. He drank $\frac{1}{6}$ of the juice. How much of the orange juice was left?

17. $5\frac{1}{8} - 2\frac{3}{4} =$

Multiply. Simplify if necessary.

18. How much is $\frac{4}{5}$ of $\frac{5}{6}$?

19. $\frac{8}{9} \times \frac{15}{16} =$

20. $2\frac{1}{2} \times 1\frac{1}{5} =$

21. $4\frac{1}{5} \times 2\frac{1}{7} =$

Divide. Simplify if necessary.

22. $\frac{4}{5} \div \frac{1}{5} =$

23. How many $\frac{1}{3}$s are in $\frac{5}{6}$?

24. $1\frac{3}{4} \div 1\frac{1}{4} =$

25. $4\frac{1}{5} \div 2\frac{1}{3} =$

Glossary

decimal
a number with one or more digits to the right of the decimal point

decimal point
a symbol used to separate the ones and tenths places in a decimal

denominator (page 8)
number below the fraction bar in a fraction

equivalent (page 10)
equal or having the same value

equivalent fractions (page 10)
fractions that name the same amount

factor (page 7)
a whole number that evenly divides into another whole number

fraction (page 7)
a number that names part of a whole or part of a group

improper fraction (page 18)
a fraction that has a numerator greater than or equal to the denominator; $\frac{4}{3}$, $\frac{9}{5}$, $\frac{37}{21}$, for example.

invert (page 56)
to turn upside down or reverse

least common multiple (LCM) (page 12)
the smallest number that is a multiple of two or more other numbers

least common denominator (LCD) (page 14)
the smallest number that the denominators of fractions being added or subtracted divide into evenly

$$\frac{1}{5} = \frac{3}{15}$$
$$\frac{1}{3} = \frac{5}{15}$$

like fractions (page 31)
fractions with the same demominator

mixed number (page 17)
a number that contains both a whole number and a fraction, for example, $3\frac{1}{2}$, $4\frac{2}{3}$, $12\frac{3}{5}$

numerator (page 8)
number above the fraction bar in a fraction

proper fraction (page 17)
a fraction that has a numerator that is less than the denominator

regrouping (page 44)
taking an amount from the whole number in a mixed number and adding it to the fraction part

$$\begin{array}{r} 4\tfrac{1}{3} = 3\tfrac{1}{3} = \tfrac{3}{3} = 3\tfrac{4}{3} \\ -1\tfrac{2}{3} \qquad\qquad\quad = 1\tfrac{2}{3} \\ \hline 2\tfrac{2}{3} \end{array}$$

rename (page 20)
change

simplest form (page 20)
a fraction in which 1 is the only number that divides evenly into the numerator and denominator

unlike fractions (page 31)
fractions that have different denominators

Equivalent Fractions and Decimals

Fraction	Decimal
$\frac{1}{2}$	0.5
$\frac{2}{2} = 1$	1.0

$\frac{1}{3}$	$0.33\overline{3}$
$\frac{2}{3}$	$0.66\overline{6}$
$\frac{3}{3} = 1$	1.0

$\frac{1}{4}$	0.25
$\frac{2}{4} = \frac{1}{2}$	0.5
$\frac{3}{4}$	0.75
$\frac{4}{4} = 1$	1.0

$\frac{1}{5}$	0.2
$\frac{2}{5}$	0.4
$\frac{3}{5}$	0.6
$\frac{4}{5}$	0.8
$\frac{5}{5} = 1$	1.0

$\frac{1}{6}$	$0.16\overline{6}$
$\frac{2}{6} = \frac{1}{3}$	$0.33\overline{3}$
$\frac{3}{6} = \frac{1}{2}$	0.5
$\frac{4}{6} = \frac{2}{3}$	$0.66\overline{6}$
$\frac{5}{6}$	$0.83\overline{3}$
$\frac{6}{6} = 1$	1.0

Fraction	Decimal
$\frac{1}{8}$	0.125
$\frac{2}{8} = \frac{1}{4}$	0.25
$\frac{3}{8}$	0.375
$\frac{4}{8} = \frac{1}{2}$	0.5
$\frac{5}{8}$	0.625
$\frac{6}{8} = \frac{3}{4}$	0.75
$\frac{7}{8}$	0.875
$\frac{8}{8} = 1$	1.0

$\frac{1}{10}$	0.1
$\frac{2}{10} = \frac{1}{5}$	0.2
$\frac{3}{10}$	0.3
$\frac{4}{10} = \frac{2}{5}$	0.4
$\frac{5}{10} = \frac{1}{2}$	0.5
$\frac{6}{10} = \frac{3}{5}$	0.6
$\frac{7}{10}$	0.7
$\frac{8}{10} = \frac{4}{5}$	0.8
$\frac{9}{10}$	0.9
$\frac{10}{10} = 1$	1.0

$\frac{1}{100}$	0.01
1	1.0

Math Toolkit

Benchmark Fractions

Some fractions are used *a lot* and are helpful in picturing other fractions. These fractions are known as **benchmark fractions.**

Knowing benchmark fractions can help you:

- compare and order fractions and mixed numbers; $\frac{3}{4} > \frac{1}{2}$
- round fractions and mixed numbers; $\frac{1}{4}$ rounds down to 0 because $\frac{1}{4}$ is closer to 0 than 1.
- estimate sums and differences of fractions and mixed numbers. $\frac{1}{3} + \frac{1}{3}$ is greater than 1 because $\frac{1}{3}$ is greater than $\frac{1}{4}$.

The fractions on the number line below are benchmark fractions. They can help you estimate fractions.

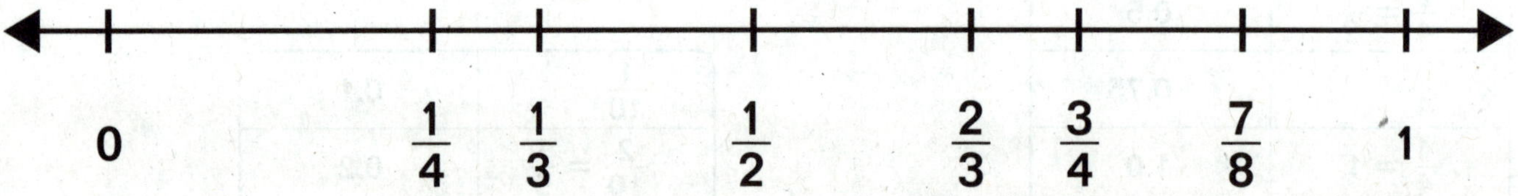

Rules for Fractions

Addition (same denominators)

$$\frac{A}{B} + \frac{C}{B} = \frac{A + C}{B}$$

$$\frac{1}{8} + \frac{2}{8} = \frac{1 + 2}{8} = \frac{3}{8}$$

Addition (different denominators)

$$\frac{A}{B} + \frac{C}{D} = \frac{AD}{BD} + \frac{BC}{BD} = \frac{AD + BC}{BD}$$

$$\frac{1}{4} + \frac{1}{3} = \frac{1 \times 3}{4 \times 3} = \frac{1 \times 4}{3 \times 4}$$

$$= \frac{3}{12} + \frac{4}{12}$$

$$= \frac{3 + 4}{12} = \frac{7}{12}$$

Subtraction (same denominators)

$$\frac{A}{B} - \frac{C}{B} = \frac{A - C}{B}$$

$$\frac{3}{4} - \frac{1}{4} = \frac{3 - 1}{4} = \frac{2}{4} = \frac{1}{2}$$

Subtraction (different denominators)

$$\frac{A}{B} - \frac{C}{D} = \frac{AD}{BD} - \frac{BC}{BD} = \frac{AD - BC}{BD}$$

$$\frac{3}{4} - \frac{1}{3} = \frac{3 \times 3}{4 \times 3} - \frac{1 \times 4}{3 \times 4}$$

$$= \frac{9}{12} + \frac{4}{12}$$

$$= \frac{9 - 4}{12} = \frac{5}{12}$$

Multiplication

$$\frac{A}{B} \times \frac{C}{D} = \frac{AC}{BD}$$

$$\frac{1}{2} \times \frac{3}{4} = \frac{1 \times 3}{2 \times 4} = \frac{3}{8}$$

Division

$$\frac{A}{B} \div \frac{C}{D} = \frac{A}{B} \times \frac{D}{C} = \frac{AD}{BC}$$

$$\frac{7}{8} \div \frac{1}{3} = \frac{7}{8} \times \frac{3}{1} = \frac{7 \times 3}{8 \times 1} = \frac{21}{8} = 2\frac{5}{8}$$

Math Toolkit

Estimation

Estimation is an important math tool that enables you to answer questions such as the following:

- What is the approximate answer to this problem?
- Am I using the right operative to solve this problem?

Using Estimation with Fractions and Decimals

The following example show you how you can round each fraction or decimal to a whole number before beginning a calculation.

Add	Estimate
$5\frac{2}{3} + 2\frac{1}{4}$	$6 + 2 = 8$
Subtract	**Estimate**
$8\frac{3}{4} - 3\frac{1}{8}$	$9 - 3 = 6$
Multiply	**Estimate**
$4\frac{7}{8} \times 3\frac{1}{5}$	$5 \times 3 = 15$
Divide	**Estimate**
$9\frac{1}{3} \div 2\frac{3}{4}$	$9 \div 3 = 3$

Key Operation Words

Word problems often contain clues that help you solve the problem. These words tell you whether you need to add, subtract, multiply, or divide. The lists of words below will help you decide which operation to use when solving word problems.

Addition

- add
- all together
- and
- both
- combined
- in all
- increase
- more
- plus
- sum
- total

Subtraction

- change (money)
- decrease
- difference
- left
- less than
- more than
- reduce
- remain or remaining
- smaller, larger, farther, nearer

Multiplication

- in all
- of
- multiply
- product
- times (as much)
- total
- twice
- whole

Division

- average
- cut
- divide
- each
- equal pieces
- every
- one
- split

Multiplication Facts

This chart can help you remember your multiplication facts. To find the product of two number, find the first factor in the left-most column. Then, find the second factor in the top row. THe product is the block where the two factors meet. The chart shows how you would find the product of 6 × 4.

	0	1	2	3	4	5	6	7	8	9	10	11	12	13	14	15
0	0	0	0	0	0	0	0	0	0	0	0	0	0	0	0	0
1	0	1	2	3	4	5	6	7	8	9	10	11	12	13	14	15
2	0	2	4	6	8	10	12	14	16	18	20	22	24	26	28	30
3	0	3	6	9	12	15	18	21	24	27	30	33	36	39	42	45
4	0	4	8	12	16	20	24	28	32	36	40	44	48	52	56	60
5	0	5	10	15	20	25	30	35	40	45	50	55	60	65	70	75
6	0	6	12	18	24	30	36	42	48	54	60	66	72	78	84	90
7	0	7	14	21	28	35	42	49	56	63	70	77	84	91	98	105
8	0	8	16	24	32	40	48	56	64	72	80	88	96	104	112	120
9	0	9	18	27	36	45	54	63	72	81	90	99	108	117	126	135
10	0	10	20	30	40	50	60	70	80	90	100	110	120	130	140	150
11	0	11	22	33	44	55	66	77	88	99	110	121	132	143	154	165
12	0	12	24	36	48	60	72	84	96	108	120	132	144	156	168	180
13	0	13	26	39	52	65	78	91	104	117	130	143	156	169	182	195
14	0	14	28	42	56	70	84	98	112	126	140	154	168	182	196	210
15	0	15	30	45	60	75	90	105	120	135	150	165	180	195	210	225

Overview • Lessons 1–4

Fractions

You already know how to add, subtract, multiply and divide whole numbers. You can learn to do the same operations with fractions. Knowing how to work with fractions is a useful everyday skill. For example, you may need $\frac{3}{4}$ cup of milk for a recipe. You may need $\frac{1}{2}$ of a yard of ribbon to make a costume. You may need to use a $\frac{3}{16}$-inch wrench for a shop project.

A **fraction** is a number that names part of a whole or part of a group. Every fraction shows 2 numbers. One number describes the part and the other number describes the whole. For example:

$$\frac{\text{part}}{\text{whole}} = \frac{3}{16}$$

The top number of a fraction is called a **numerator.**
The bottom number of a fraction is called a **denominator.**

3 ← numerator
16 ← denominator

YOU KNOW

- That each product in a multiplication table is a multiple
- That a number multiplied or divided by 1 remains the same number
- How to find the greatest common factor (GCF) of 2 numbers

YOU WILL LEARN

- How to write fractions to represent part of a whole or a group
- How to find the least common multiple
- How to find equivalent fractions
- How to compare and order fractions.

Remember the BASICS

Multiply.

1. $12 \times 3 = 36$ **2.** $24 \times 6 =$ **3.** $19 \times 4 =$

4. $16 \times 11 =$ **5.** $32 \times 13 =$ **6.** $63 \times 2 =$

Divide.

7. $15 \div 3 = 5$ **8.** $22 \div 11 =$ **9.** $20 \div 4 =$

10. $63 \div 7 =$ **11.** $121 \div 11 =$ **12.** $483 \div 21 =$

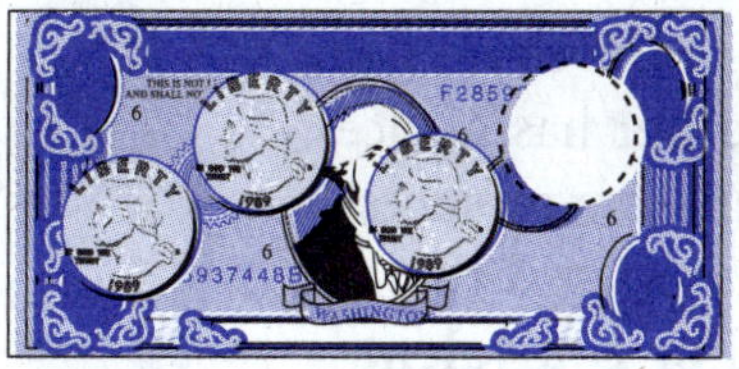

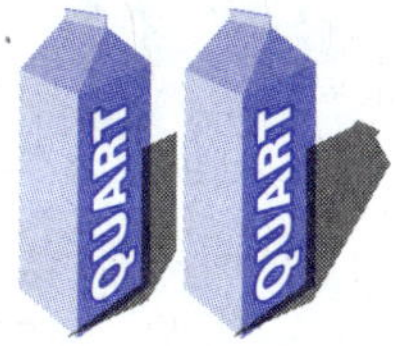

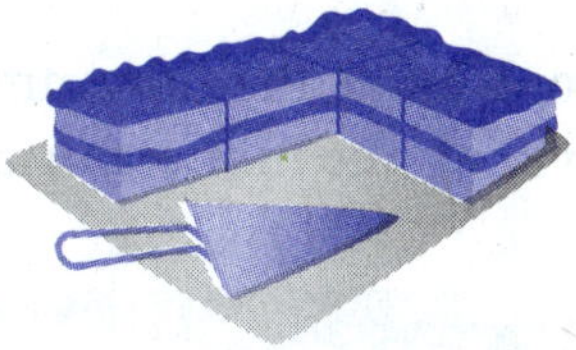

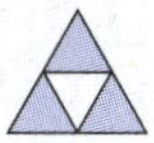 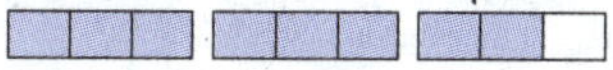 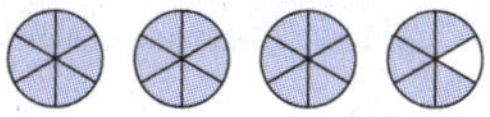 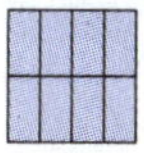 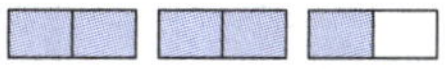 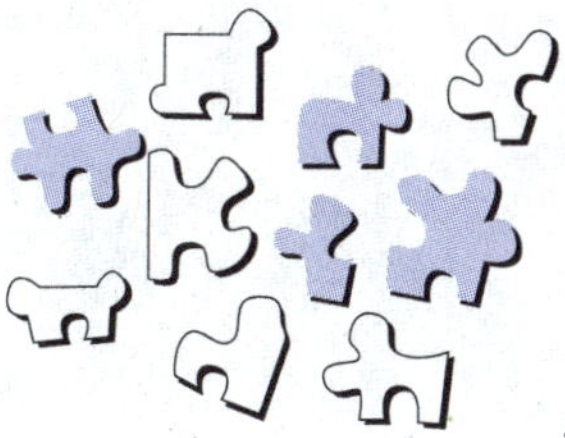 # Practice

Building Skills

Find an equivalent fraction.

1. $\frac{4}{8}$ $\div \frac{4}{4} = \frac{1}{2}$
2. $\frac{10}{15}$
3. $\frac{6}{12}$
4. $\frac{18}{24}$

Circle the equivalent fraction.

5. $\frac{1}{2} = \frac{3}{10} \quad \frac{6}{12} \quad \frac{4}{7} \quad \frac{3}{9} \quad \frac{2}{8}$
6. $\frac{3}{5} = \frac{3}{10} \quad \frac{7}{12} \quad \frac{6}{10} \quad \frac{6}{20} \quad \frac{10}{15}$
7. $\frac{2}{3} = \frac{8}{10} \quad \frac{6}{9} \quad \frac{4}{12} \quad \frac{3}{9} \quad \frac{2}{24}$
8. $\frac{9}{10} = \frac{3}{4} \quad \frac{18}{21} \quad \frac{4}{5} \quad \frac{3}{9} \quad \frac{27}{30}$

Problem Solving

Find the equivalent fraction.

9. Manny has read 6 of the 10 books in a popular mystery series. How many fifths is this?

   $\frac{6}{10} = \frac{3}{5}$

10. Anna has converted $\frac{5}{8}$ of her old videocassettes to DVDs. How many sixteenths is this?

11. Vinny shelved 30 of the 40 books that were returned to the library today. How many fourths is this?

12. Raquel invited 20 people to her party and 16 of them showed up. Write an equivalent fraction to describe how many of the invited people came to the party.

13. You have collected 25 of the 50 state quarters. Write an equivalent fraction to show this number.

14. You did 25 of the 30 push-ups required in gym class. Find an equivalent fraction when 5 is the numerator.

Math Toolkit

Estimation

Estimation is an important math tool that enables you to answer questions such as the following:

- What is the approximate answer to this problem?
- Am I using the right operative to solve this problem?

Using Estimation with Fractions and Decimals

The following example show you how you can round each fraction or decimal to a whole number before beginning a calculation.

Add	Estimate
$5\frac{2}{3}$ $+2\frac{1}{4}$	6 +2 8
Subtract	**Estimate**
$8\frac{3}{4}$ $-3\frac{1}{8}$	9 −3 6
Multiply	**Estimate**
$4\frac{7}{8} \times 3\frac{1}{5}$	$5 \times 3 = 15$
Divide	**Estimate**
$9\frac{1}{3} \div 2\frac{3}{4}$	$9 \div 3 = 3$

UNIT 1 Review

Write the proper or improper fraction that names the shaded part.

1. 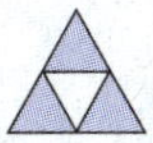 ____________

2.  ____________

3. 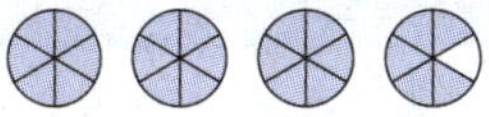 ____________

4.  ____________

Write the mixed number that names the shaded part.

5.  ____________

6.  ____________

Change each fraction to a whole number or mixed number.

7. $\frac{9}{4} =$

8. $\frac{15}{12} =$

9. $\frac{22}{5} =$

10. $\frac{33}{6} =$

Change each mixed number to an improper fraction.

11. $3\frac{1}{4} =$

12. $2\frac{5}{8} =$

13. $7\frac{1}{2} =$

14. $10\frac{3}{4} =$

Simplify each fraction.

15. $\frac{10}{12} =$

16. $\frac{9}{15} =$

17. $\frac{12}{16} =$

18. $\frac{16}{24} =$

Find an equivalent fraction with the given denominator.

19. $\frac{2}{5} = \frac{\quad}{15}$

20. $\frac{3}{4} = \frac{\quad}{12}$

21. $\frac{2}{3} = \frac{\quad}{12}$

22. $\frac{1}{4} = \frac{\quad}{20}$

Compare each pair of fractions. Write >, <, or =.

23. $\frac{5}{6} \; \square \; \frac{1}{2}$

24. $\frac{2}{5} \; \square \; \frac{1}{2}$

25. $\frac{5}{8} \; \square \; \frac{2}{3}$

26. $\frac{9}{24} \; \square \; \frac{3}{8}$

LESSON 4 Comparing and Ordering Fractions

At lunch you decide to share 2 granola bars with your friends. One friend gets $\frac{2}{3}$ of 1 bar. The other friend gets $\frac{3}{4}$ of the other bar. Look at the granola bars. You can see that $\frac{3}{4} > \frac{2}{3}$

3/4

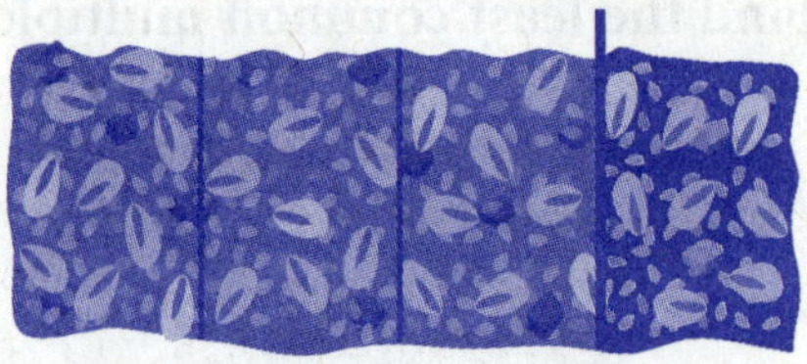

2/3

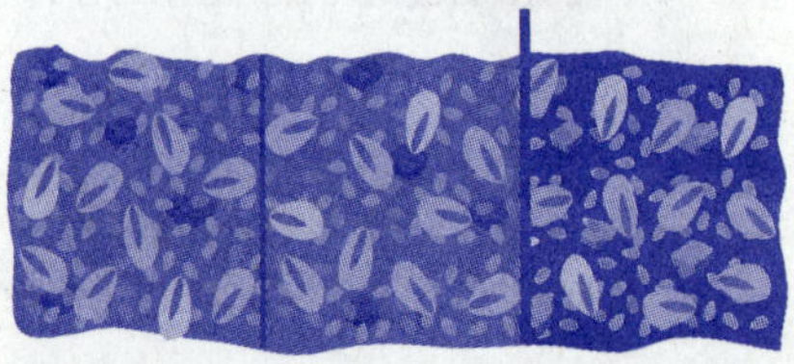

To compare fractions, the fractions must have the same denominator. You can use your knowledge of equivalent fractions to rewrite each fraction, so that it has same denominator. To find the common denominator, use the least common multiple (LCM) of the denominators. This is also called the **least common denominator** (LCD). When the denominators are the same, compare the numerators to see which fraction is greater.

$$\frac{\text{numerator}}{\text{denominator}} = \frac{3}{4}$$

Example

Compare. Use <, >, or = signs.

$\frac{3}{7}$ $\frac{2}{5}$

STEP 1 Find the least common denominator (LCD).

List the multiples of 5 and 7.

5: 5, 10, 15, 20, 25, 30, 35, 40. . .

7: 7, 14, 21, 28, 35, 42, 49, 56. . .

The least common multiple (LCM) of the denominators is 35. So the LCD is 35.

STEP 2 Write equivalent fractions using the LCD as the new denominator.

$\frac{3}{7} = \frac{}{35}$ $\frac{2}{5} = \frac{}{35}$

STEP 3 Divide the LCD by the denominators.

$35 \div 7 = 5$ $35 \div 5 = 7$

STEP 4 Multiply the numerator and denominator of each fraction by the answers in Step 3.

$\frac{3}{7} \times \frac{5}{5} = \frac{15}{35}$ $\frac{2}{5} \times \frac{7}{7} = \frac{14}{35}$

STEP 5 Compare the numerators.

$\frac{3}{7} > \frac{2}{5}$

$15 > 14$, so $\frac{15}{35} > \frac{14}{35}$

ON YOUR OWN

Kirsten has completed $\frac{1}{3}$ of her homework. Brendan has completed $\frac{2}{5}$ of his homework. Use <, >, or = to show who has completed more homework.

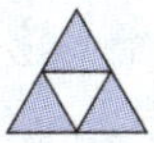 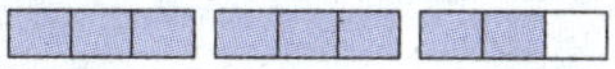 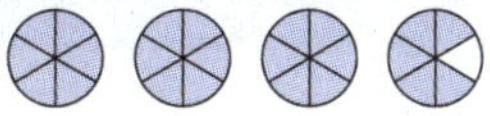 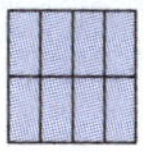 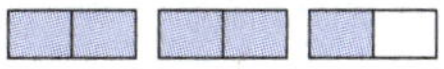 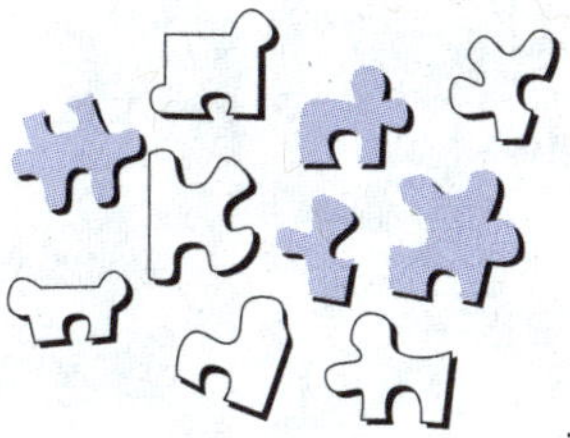 ## Key Operation Words

Word problems often contain clues that help you solve the problem. These words tell you whether you need to add, subtract, multiply, or divide. The lists of words below will help you decide which operation to use when solving word problems.

Addition	Subtraction
add	change (money)
all together	decrease
and	difference
both	left
combined	less than
in all	more than
increase	reduce
more	remain or remaining
plus	smaller, larger, farther, nearer
sum	
total	

Multiplication	Division
in all	average
of	cut
multiply	divide
product	each
times (as much)	equal pieces
total	every
twice	one
whole	split

Overview • Lessons 1–4

Fractions

You already know how to add, subtract, multiply and divide whole numbers. You can learn to do the same operations with fractions. Knowing how to work with fractions is a useful everyday skill. For example, you may need $\frac{3}{4}$ cup of milk for a recipe. You may need $\frac{1}{2}$ of a yard of ribbon to make a costume. You may need to use a $\frac{3}{16}$-inch wrench for a shop project.

A **fraction** is a number that names part of a whole or part of a group. Every fraction shows 2 numbers. One number describes the part and the other number describes the whole. For example:

$$\frac{\text{part}}{\text{whole}} = \frac{3}{16}$$

The top number of a fraction is called a **numerator.**
The bottom number of a fraction is called a **denominator.**

$$\frac{3}{16} \begin{matrix} \leftarrow \text{numerator} \\ \leftarrow \text{denominator} \end{matrix}$$

YOU KNOW

- That each product in a multiplication table is a multiple
- That a number multiplied or divided by 1 remains the same number
- How to find the greatest common factor (GCF) of 2 numbers

YOU WILL LEARN

- How to write fractions to represent part of a whole or a group
- How to find the least common multiple
- How to find equivalent fractions
- How to compare and order fractions.

Remember the BASICS

Multiply.

1. $12 \times 3 =$ 36
2. $24 \times 6 =$
3. $19 \times 4 =$
4. $16 \times 11 =$
5. $32 \times 13 =$
6. $63 \times 2 =$

Divide.

7. $15 \div 3 =$ 5
8. $22 \div 11 =$
9. $20 \div 4 =$
10. $63 \div 7 =$
11. $121 \div 11 =$
12. $483 \div 21 =$

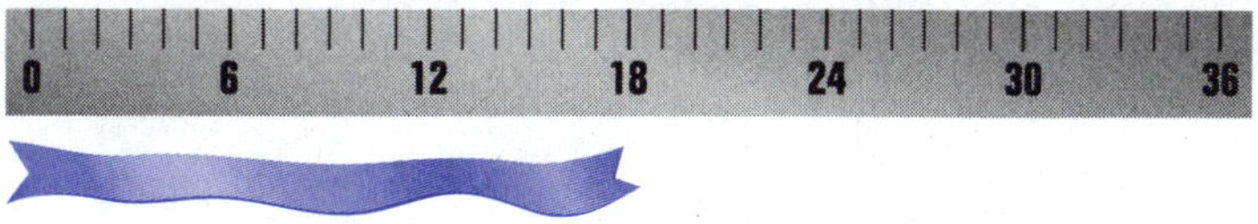

Write the proper or improper fraction that names the shaded part.

1. 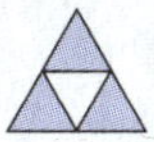 ______

2. 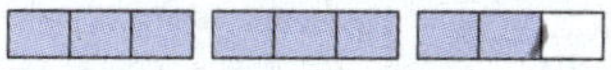 ______

3. 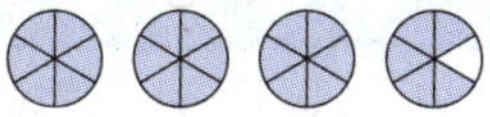 ______

4.  ______

Write the mixed number that names the shaded part.

5.  ______

6.  ______

Change each fraction to a whole number or mixed number.

7. $\frac{9}{4} =$ 8. $\frac{15}{12} =$ 9. $\frac{22}{5} =$ 10. $\frac{33}{6} =$

Change each mixed number to an improper fraction.

11. $3\frac{1}{4} =$ 12. $2\frac{5}{8} =$ 13. $7\frac{1}{2} =$ 14. $10\frac{3}{4} =$

Simplify each fraction.

15. $\frac{10}{12} =$ 16. $\frac{9}{15} =$ 17. $\frac{12}{16} =$ 18. $\frac{16}{24} =$

Find an equivalent fraction with the given denominator.

19. $\frac{2}{5} = \frac{}{15}$ 20. $\frac{3}{4} = \frac{}{12}$ 21. $\frac{2}{3} = \frac{}{12}$ 22. $\frac{1}{4} = \frac{}{20}$

Compare each pair of fractions. Write >, <, or =.

23. $\frac{5}{6}$ ☐ $\frac{1}{2}$ 24. $\frac{2}{5}$ ☐ $\frac{1}{2}$ 25. $\frac{5}{8}$ ☐ $\frac{2}{3}$ 26. $\frac{9}{24}$ ☐ $\frac{3}{8}$

Overview • Lessons 5 – 7

Mixed Numbers

You are going down the highway. A sign says that the next 2 exits are $\frac{1}{2}$ mile and $2\frac{1}{2}$ miles away.

You learned that $\frac{1}{2}$ is a fraction. It is a **proper fraction** because the numerator is smaller than the denominator. $2\frac{1}{2}$ is a mixed number. A **mixed number** is a whole number and a proper fraction.

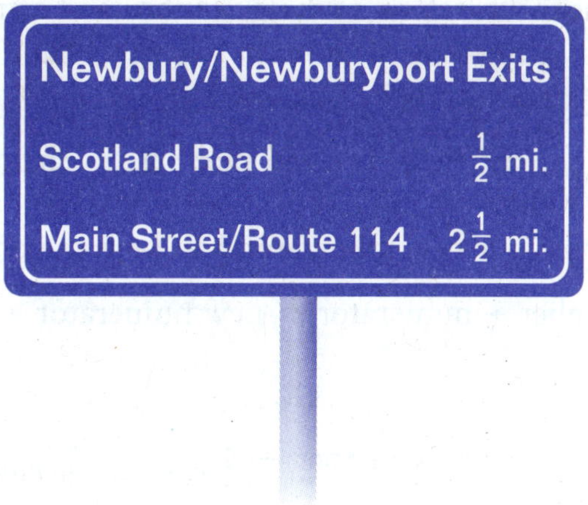

whole number $\rightarrow 2\frac{1}{2}$ $\leftarrow$ numerator, $\leftarrow$ denominator

YOU KNOW

- How to simplify fractions
- That when the numerator is the same as the denominator, the fraction equals 1

YOU WILL LEARN

- How to rename an improper fraction
- How to change mixed numbers into improper fractions
- How to simplify mixed numbers

Remember the BASICS

Simplify each fraction.

1. $\frac{4}{10} =$

   $\frac{4}{10} \div \frac{2}{2} = \frac{2}{5}$

2. $\frac{3}{6} =$
3. $\frac{16}{18} =$
4. $\frac{9}{9} =$
5. $\frac{8}{16} =$
6. $\frac{12}{15} =$
7. $\frac{10}{10} =$
8. $\frac{15}{20} =$
9. $\frac{21}{24} =$
10. $\frac{16}{16} =$
11. $\frac{14}{21} =$
12. $\frac{20}{25} =$
13. $\frac{24}{30} =$
14. $\frac{20}{20} =$
15. $\frac{15}{24} =$
16. $\frac{30}{40} =$

STECK-VAUGHN

TOP LINE *Math*

Top Line Math Diagnostic Teacher's Guide

To the Teacher

This guide consists of an answer key, a correlation chart, and answer sheet for Steck-Vaughn's *Top Line Math Diagnostic*. You may duplicate any of these pages as you need for classroom use.

The diagnostic serves as a placement test for the *Top Line Math* series. Results from the diagnostic will help you to individualize instruction for your students based on specific skill areas where they need intervention. The diagnostic, together with the pretest and post test in each of the ten books, will enable you to target appropriate instruction for accelerating your students toward proficiency and success in math.

- Students can use the **Answer Sheet** to circle the correct choice for each item on the diagnostic.
- The **Diagnostic Correlation Chart** will help you assess your students' skill levels and determine where to place them within the Steck-Vaughn *Top Line Math* series. Students scoring fewer than three out of four correctly for the items in any given book need to focus on developing those foundational math skills.
- The **Answer Key** provides worked-out solutions that can be used as an opportunity for individualized instruction.

Harcourt Achieve
Rigby • Saxon • Steck-Vaughn

www.HarcourtAchieve.com
1.800.531.5015

ISBN 1-4190-0434-4

9 781419 004346

1. **D** $\begin{array}{r} 83.057 \\ +16.02 \\ \hline 99.077 \end{array}$

2. **B** $\begin{array}{r} 9.68 \\ -4.19 \\ \hline 5.49 \end{array}$

3. **B** $6 \text{ ft} \times 3 \text{ ft} = 18 \text{ ft}^2$

4. **C** $1\frac{1}{5} \times 3\frac{2}{3} = \frac{6}{5} \times \frac{11}{3} = \frac{66}{15} = 4\frac{4}{10}$ or $4\frac{2}{5}$

5. **A** $\cancel{3}^{2}\frac{1}{3} = \frac{\cancel{4}^{+12}}{12}$ $\qquad \frac{16}{12}$

$2\frac{3}{4} = \frac{9}{12}$ $\qquad \begin{array}{r} \frac{16}{12} \\ -\frac{9}{12} \\ \hline \frac{7}{12} \end{array}$

6. **D** $3\frac{3}{4} \div 4\frac{2}{7} = \frac{15}{4} \div \frac{30}{7} = \frac{15}{4} \times \frac{7}{30} = \frac{105}{120} = \frac{7}{8}$

7. **B** $90 \times 3 = 270$

8. **A** cheeseburger and fries + a soft drink = 1200 calories; B = 1150 cal.; C = 1100 cal., D = 1045 cal.

9. **A** Option **B** is $\frac{4}{100}$; **C** is $\frac{4}{10}$.

10. **B** $14.28 \div 2.1 = 6.8$

11. **A** $C = (86 - 32)\frac{5}{9} = 30°$

$C = (54)\frac{5}{9}$

$C = \frac{270}{9}$

$C = 30$

12. **B**

13. **C** $\frac{8}{12} = \frac{2}{3}$

14. **D** $\frac{7}{x} = \frac{49}{63}$

$49x = 7 \times 63$

$49x = 441$

$x = \frac{441}{49}$

$x = 9$

Alternate Solution, simplify $\frac{49}{63}$: $\frac{(49 \div 7)}{(63 \div 7)} = \frac{7}{9}$

15. **D** $w \times w = w^2$

16. **C** $|-1| = 1$

17. **C** Giant-Brewers game took in twice as much money.

18. **A** $\frac{12}{80} = 0.15$

$0.15 \times 100 = 15\%$

19. **A** $9 \div 1000 = 0.009$

20. **B** 11:07 − 6:55 = 10:67 − 6:55 = 4 hours and 12 minutes

21. **D** 1 out of 4 $= \frac{1}{4} = 0.25$, $0.25 \times 100 = 25\%$

22. **A** $-54 \div 9 = -6$

23. **B** $I = prt = \$275 \times 0.03 \times 2 = \$16.50$

24. **C** $-4 > -6$

25. **A** $\frac{(2 \times 2 \times 4 \times -(-1))}{(2 \times 2)} = \frac{16}{4} = 4$

26. **D** Median is the middle number in an ordered set of data. 300, 500, 550, 575, 600; 550 is the middle number.

27. **D** $7w - 21 - 3w = 4w - 21$

28. **C** $A = 3.14 \times 5 \times 5 = 78.5$

29. **D**

30. **C** Ladder = c, $7^2 + 22^2 = c^2$

$c^2 = 49 + 484$

$c = \sqrt{533} = 23$ ft

31. **C** $\frac{3}{6} = \frac{1}{2}$ or 50%

32. **C**

33. **A** $x + 10 > 45 - 10$

$x > 35$

34. **A** Solve for *y*, when $x = 0, 1, 2$.

35. **C** Have students trace up vertical line at 4 on the *x*-axis (Week).

36. **C** $y = (10 \times 2) - 5 = 15$ and $y = (10 \times 4) - 5 = 35$

37. **B** $x + (2x - 10)$ To double-check, solve when $x = 25$.

First rocking chair (x) costs \$25; the second chair (2x − 10) costs \$40.

38. **C** $3 + 8 + + 12 + 1 + 9 + 7 = 40$

39. **B**

40. **A**

Correlation Chart

Name ______________________ Date ______________________

BOOK	INVENTORY ITEMS	TOTAL CORRECT
Number Concepts	15, 16, 22, 24	______ out of 4
Fractions	4, 5, 6, 12	______ out of 4
Decimals	1, 2, 9, 10	______ out of 4
Ratios and Percents	13, 14, 18, 23	______ out of 4
Measurement	11, 19, 20, 38	______ out of 4
Geometry	3, 28, 30, 32	______ out of 4
Data, Tables, and Graphs	7, 8, 35, 39	______ out of 4
Pre-Algebra	25, 27, 33, 34	______ out of 4
Data Analysis and Probability	17, 21, 26, 31	______ out of 4
Mathematical Reasoning	29, 36, 37, 40	______ out of 4

Answer Sheet

Name ______________________ Date ______________________

Circle the correct answer.

1.	A	B	C	D	**21.**	A	B	C	D
2.	A	B	C	D	**22.**	A	B	C	D
3.	A	B	C	D	**23.**	A	B	C	D
4.	A	B	C	D	**24.**	A	B	C	D
5.	A	B	C	D	**25.**	A	B	C	D
6.	A	B	C	D	**26.**	A	B	C	D
7.	A	B	C	D	**27.**	A	B	C	D
8.	A	B	C	D	**28.**	A	B	C	D
9.	A	B	C	D	**29.**	A	B	C	D
10.	A	B	C	D	**30.**	A	B	C	D
11.	A	B	C	D	**31.**	A	B	C	D
12.	A	B	C	D	**32.**	A	B	C	D
13.	A	B	C	D	**33.**	A	B	C	D
14.	A	B	C	D	**34.**	A	B	C	D
15.	A	B	C	D	**35.**	A	B	C	D
16.	A	B	C	D	**36.**	A	B	C	D
17.	A	B	C	D	**37.**	A	B	C	D
18.	A	B	C	D	**38.**	A	B	C	D
19.	A	B	C	D	**39.**	A	B	C	D
20.	A	B	C	D	**40.**	A	B	C	D

STECK-VAUGHN
TOP LINE Math

Diagnostic

Name ______________________ Date ______________________

To the Student

Taking the *Top Line Math Diagnostic* will help you find out which math skills you need to develop to succeed in school. You have 40 minutes to answer 40 multiple-choice items. Work carefully and answer as many questions as you can. Use the space in this booklet to work out the problems. Circle your answers on the answer sheet your teacher gives you.

Example:

If groceries cost $15.75, and you pay with a $20.00 bill, how much change should you get back?

A. $3.25

B. $4.25

C. $4.75

D. $5.25

(on answer sheet)

A (B) C D

The correct answer is **B $4.25**. You would circle **B** on the answer sheet.

4500358139

ISBN 1-4190-0433-6

9 781419 004339

Directions: Read and answer the questions. Circle the letter of the correct answer on your answer sheet.

1. Add.

$$\begin{array}{r} 83.057 \\ +16.02 \\ \hline \end{array}$$

A. 0.99077
B. 9.9077
C. 90.77
D. 99.077

2. Subtract.

$$\begin{array}{r} 9.68 \\ -4.19 \\ \hline \end{array}$$

A. 0.0549
B. 5.49
C. 54.9
D. 549

3. Which of the following is the area of a rectangle that is 6 ft long and 3 ft wide?

A. 9 sq ft
B. 18 sq ft
C. 21 sq ft
D. 25 sq ft

4. Multiply. $1\frac{1}{5} \times 3\frac{2}{3}$

A. $2\frac{3}{5}$
B. $3\frac{2}{5}$
C. $4\frac{2}{5}$
D. $5\frac{3}{5}$

5. Subtract.

$$\begin{array}{r} 3\frac{1}{3} \\ -2\frac{3}{4} \\ \hline \end{array}$$

A. $\frac{7}{12}$
B. $1\frac{5}{12}$
C. $1\frac{7}{12}$
D. $7\frac{1}{12}$

6. Divide. $3\frac{3}{4} \div 4\frac{2}{7}$

A. $\frac{1}{3}$
B. $\frac{1}{8}$
C. $\frac{5}{8}$
D. $\frac{7}{8}$

Refer to the following information to answer questions 7 and 8. The circle graph below shows the number of calories in various foods you could eat in a day.

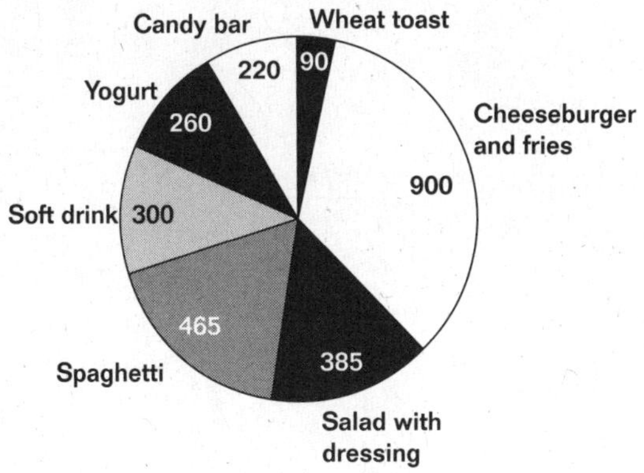

7. According to the graph, how many slices of wheat toast can you eat to get 270 calories?

A. 2
B. 3
C. 4
D. 5

8. Which meal below has the most calories?

A. cheeseburger and fries, and a soft drink
B. spaghetti, salad with dressing, and a soft drink
C. 2 yogurts, 4 slices of wheat toast, and candy bar
D. 1 yogurt, 2 slices of wheat toast, salad with dressing, and candy bar

9. What is $\frac{4}{1{,}000}$ written as a decimal?

A. 0.004
B. 0.04
C. 0.4
D. 4

10. Divide. $2.1\overline{)14.28}$

A. 0.68
B. 6.8
C. 68
D. 680

11. Using the formula $C = \frac{5}{9}(F - 32)$, which of the following is the value of C when F is 86°?

A. $C = 30°$
B. $C = 32°$
C. $C = 45°$
D. $C = 54°$

12. Which of the following shows 47% written as a decimal and as a fraction?

A. $0.047, 4\frac{7}{10}$
B. $0.47, \frac{47}{100}$
C. $0.47, 4\frac{7}{10}$
D. $47.0, \frac{47}{100}$

13. Which of the following shows the ratio of 8 to 12?

A. $\frac{1}{3}$
B. $\frac{1}{4}$
C. $\frac{2}{3}$
D. $\frac{3}{4}$

14. Solve. $\frac{7}{x} = \frac{49}{63}$

A. $x = 4$
B. $x = 5$
C. $x = 8$
D. $x = 9$

15. Which of the following shows $w \times w$ written using exponents?

A. 2
B. 2^w
C. $2w$
D. w^2

16. Solve. $|-1| =$

A. -3
B. -1
C. 1
D. 2

Use the following information to answer number 17. The graph shows the amount of money taken in at two major league baseball games in one night.

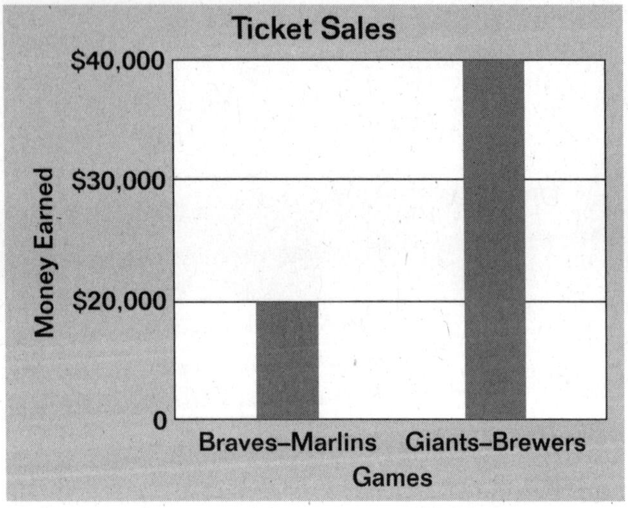

17. Which of these statements is true?

A. The Giants-Brewers game took in half as much money as the Braves-Marlins game.
B. The Braves-Marlins game took in $15,000 more than the Giants-Brewers game.
C. The Giants-Brewers game took in twice as much as the Braves-Marlins game.
D. The Braves-Marlins game took in one-third less that the Giants-Brewers game.

18. 12 is what percent of 80?

A. 15%
B. 30%
C. 68%
D. 92%

19. 9 milliliters = ______ liters

A. 0.009
B. 0.9
C. 0.09
D. 9000

20. On Saturday Brigitte clocked in at her job at 6:55 AM. She clocked out at 11:07 AM. How long did Brigitte work?

A. 4 hours and 21 minutes
B. 4 hours and 12 minutes
C. 5 hours and 12 minutes
D. 5 hours and 21 minutes

21. Five friends are planning a trip. To decide who will drive, they put five cards—all the same size—in a bag. One card has the word *drive.* The other four cards are blank. Each person will pick a card until someone picks the card with *drive* on it.

The first card picked is blank. What is the probability that the second card picked will have the word *drive?*

A. 10%
B. 15%
C. 20%
D. 25%

22. Divide $-54 \div 9$

A. -6
B. -5
C. 6
D. 9

23. Find the simple interest of $275 at 3% for 2 years.

A. $8.25
B. $16.50
C. $82.50
D. $165.00

24. Compare. Use $=$, $<$, $>$, or $\approx$.

-4 ☐ -6

A. $=$
B. $<$
C. $>$
D. $\approx$

25. Evaluate $\frac{2bc(-a)}{2b}$ if $a = -1, b = 2, c = 4$

A. 4
B. -1
C. 2
D. 3

26. The graph below shows countries that supply oil to the United States. Which amount of oil best shows the median?

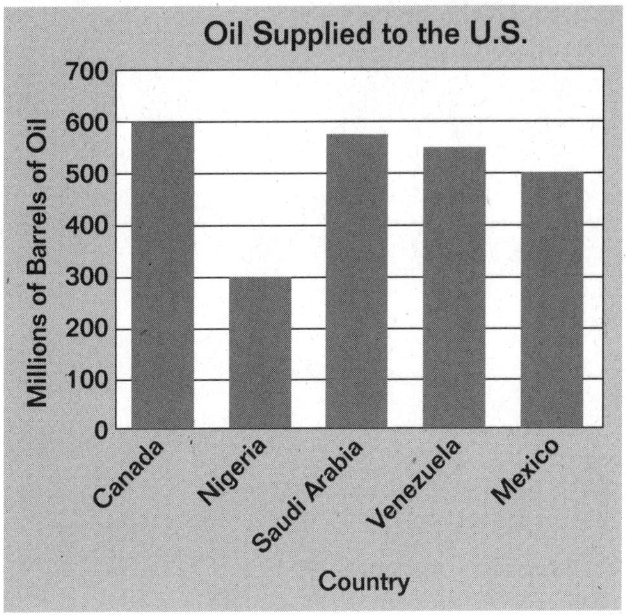

A. 400 million barrels
B. 450 million barrels
C. 500 million barrels
D. 550 million barrels

27. Simplify $7(w - 3) - 3w$

A. $21 - 4w$
B. $4w - 10$
C. $4 + 4w$
D. $4w - 21$

28. What is the area of a circle with a radius 5 inches long? Use 3.14 for π.

A. 15.7 sq in.
B. 31.4 sq in.
C. 78.5 sq in.
D. 314 sq in.

29. This is a drawing of a solid figure built with cubes.

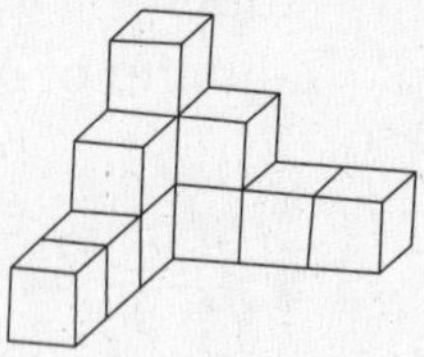

Which drawing below shows the shape when viewed from above?

A. 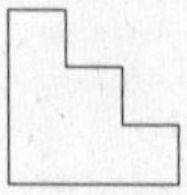

C. 

B. 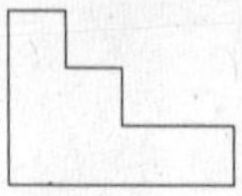

D. 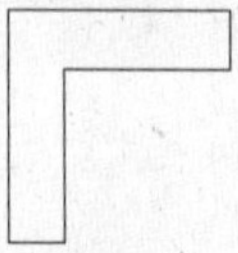

30. Look at the picture to the right. To the nearest foot, how long is the ladder that reaches the third floor window?

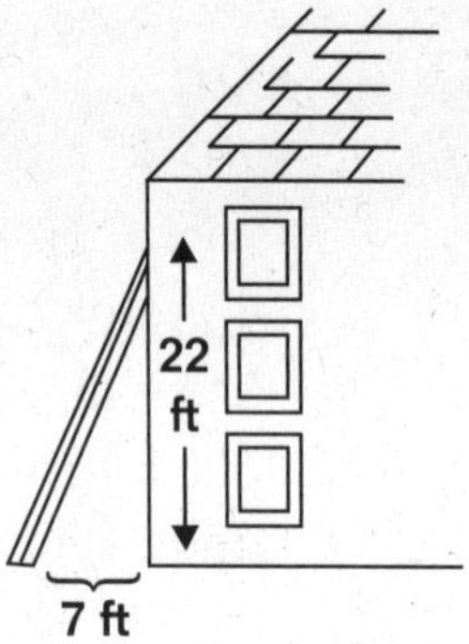

A. 15 ft
B. 19 ft
C. 23 ft
D. 29 ft

31. The spinner shown has 6 equal sections. What is the probability that the wheel will stop on a 2?

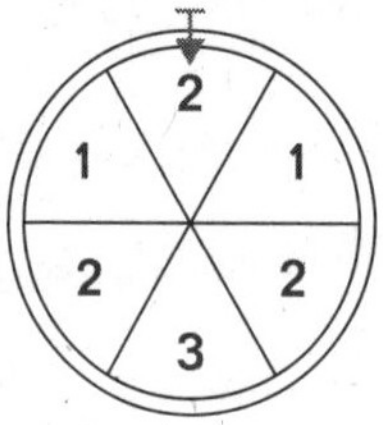

A. $\frac{1}{6}$ or $16\frac{2}{3}\%$

B. $\frac{1}{3}$ or $33\frac{1}{3}\%$

C. $\frac{1}{2}$ or 50%

D. 2 or 200%

32. In the figure below, line *a* is parallel to line *b*.

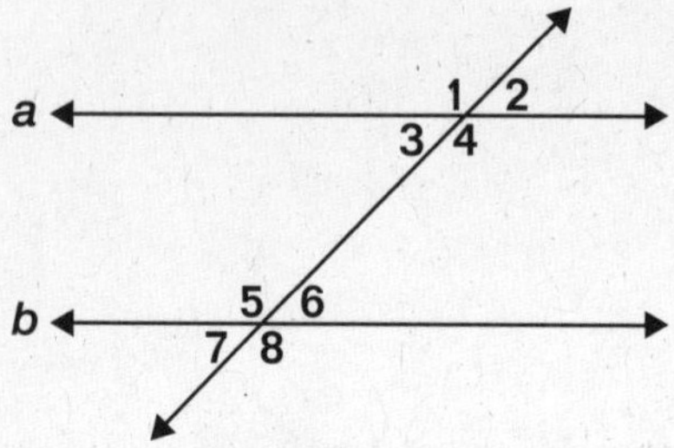

Which of the following statements is true?

A. $\angle 6$ is supplementary to $\angle 7$
B. $\angle 1$ is complementary to $\angle 2$
C. $\angle 2 + \angle 5 = 180°$
D. $\angle 1 = \angle 6$

33. Solve for *x*. $x + 10 > 45$

A. $x > 35$
B. $x < 35$
C. $x \geq 45$
D. $x = 35$

34. Which of the following is a graph of $-2x - y = -7$?

A. 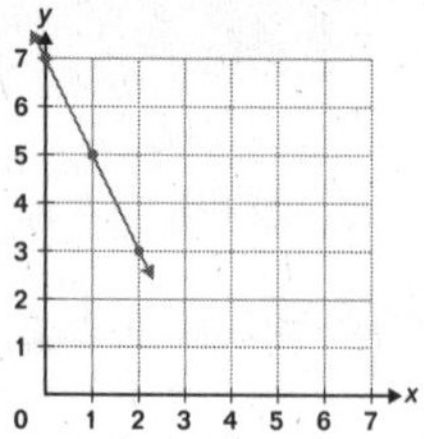

C. 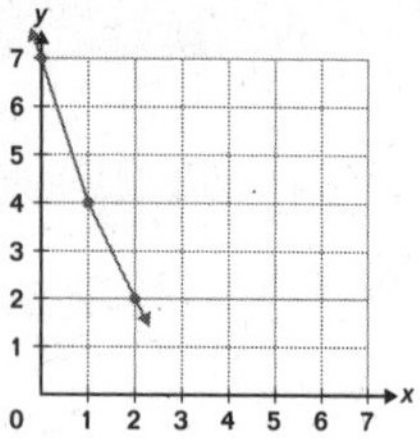

B. 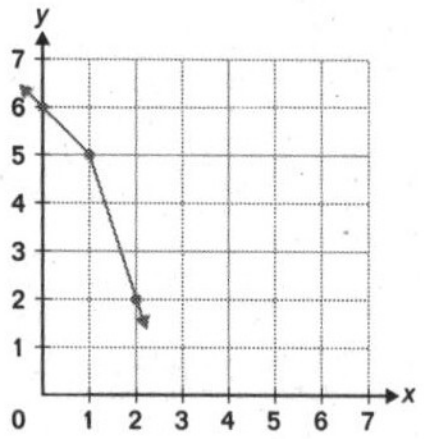

D. 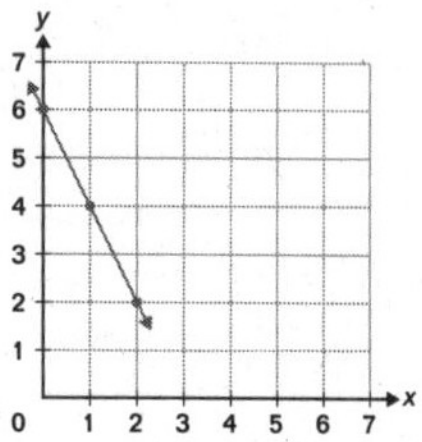

35. According to the graph, how many miles did Hamid walk each day during week 4 of his exercise program?

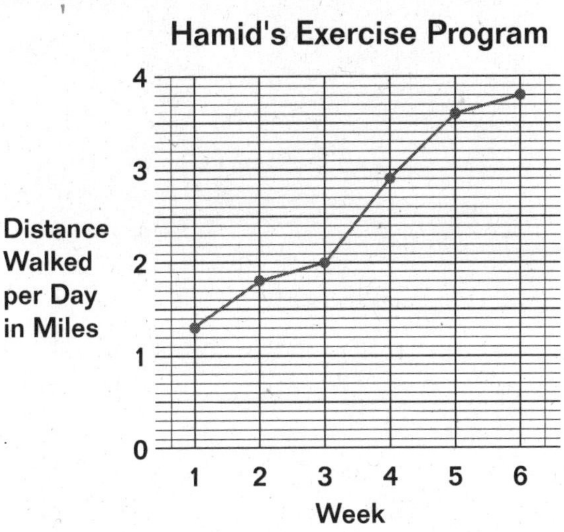

A. 2.4 miles
B. 2.5 miles
C. 2.9 miles
D. 3.1 miles

36. The function $y = 10x - 5$ has been used to create the following table. Which numbers are missing from the table?

x	−2	0	2	4	6
y	−25	−5			55

A. 5 and 25
B. 10 and 30
C. 15 and 35
D. 20 and 40

37. Eva bought 2 rocking chairs for $65. The price for the second rocking chair was $10 less than twice the cost of the first rocking chair. Which equation below could you use to find the amount of the first rocking chair?

A. $3x = 65 - 10$
B. $x+(2x-10) = 65$
C. $2(x - 10) = 65$
D. $x(x - 10) = 65$

38. What is the perimeter of this figure?

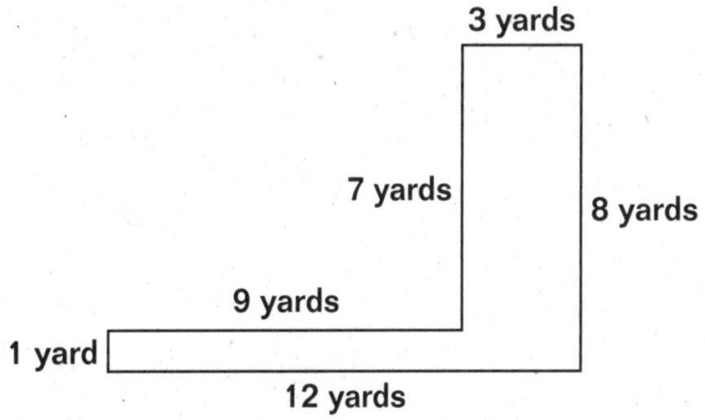

A. 31 yards
B. 39 yards
C. 40 yards
D. 50 yards

39. How many more students ate breakfast at the cafeteria in September than in August?

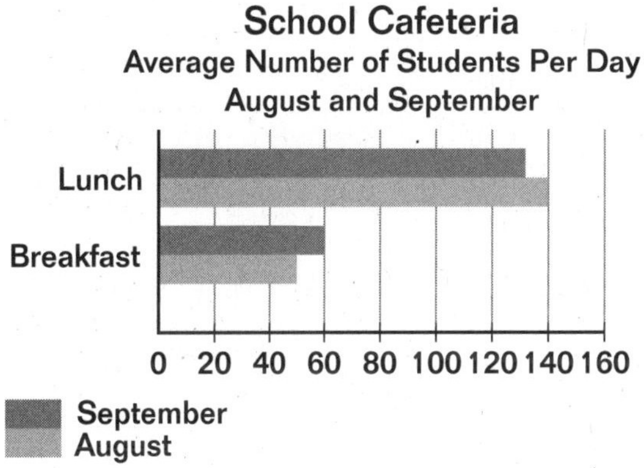

A. 5
B. 10
C. 20
D. 40

40. Roy needs $35 to get his new jacket and jeans off layaway. He has already paid $65. Which arithmetic expression shows the total cost of Roy's new clothes?

A. $65 + 35$
B. $65 - 35$
C. $35 \div 65$
D. 35×65

Harcourt Achieve
Rigby • Saxon • Steck-Vaughn

www.HarcourtAchieve.com
1.800.531.5015